Way to Go

Way to Go

SURVIVING IN THIS WORLD UNTIL SOMETHING BETTER COMES ALONG

Wally Phillips

WILLIAM MORROW AND COMPANY, INC.
New York

To Kids, including Holly, Todd and Jenny,
Custodians of Tomorrow

Library of Congress Cataloging in Publication Data

Phillips, Wally.
  Way to go.

  I. Title.
PN6162.P5   1985   818'.5402   84-22783
ISBN 0-688-03907-3

Printed in the United States of America

First Edition

1 2 3 4 5 6 7 8 9 10

BOOK DESIGN BY BERNARD SCHLEIFER

Acknowledgments

Dr. Alan Blum
Dr. Willard Fry
Dr. Lee Gladstone
Dr. Robert Schmitz
Dr. Sidney Schnoll
Dr. Brenda Clorfene Solomon

For not losing patience . . . or patients.

Thanks to the celebrities (1-10) who permitted their names to appear.

Special thanks to Marilyn Miller, a support system that never malfunctions. The Producer who always Produces.

Mountaintop Esteem and the deepest appreciation to Dan Fabian, Friend, Broadcasting Executive, Brain, for the willingness to share his wit, his wisdom, his wizardry with words.

Contents

Prologue

Face it.

> There is no such thing as time.
> It doesn't exist.
> Every second of the past is gone . . . forever.
> The future isn't here yet . . . a total unknown.
> And now is then before you can even say it.

So? What did you expect for the price of some cancer sticks, the Wisdom of Sol? No problem, it is in here somewhere along with juicy bits and pieces from the likes of A. Einstein, S. Freud, J. Christ, M. Gandhi, G. Steinhem, T. Aquinas, D. Fossey, J. Drahman (who makes the author's all-time who's who on the strength of having, as an incredibly well-endowed fellow third grader, helped him appreciate the positive aspects of gender differentiations. Thanks, June, wherever you are) and that ultimate humanitarian-philosopher H. Hefner, who once uttered the immortal clauses "When all is said and done, it isn't how you played the game that counts. It's—did you score?" Your act may be poles apart from his, but whatever rules you run by, we are here to work on your game.

No small feat when you consider that there have already been

842,605 how to almost everythings published and that every one of them has had a chance to let you in on the one and only, official, inside secret to such important life-style calisthenics as coping, keeping up, getting ahead, asserting, laying back, charging forth, recognizing potential, prioritizing, self-starting, self-stopping, making it with women, making it with men, making it with all natural ingredients, and getting in touch with your feelings, whatever that means.

All those self-help specials are the fruit of a megabucks industry that tries its unsuccessful damnedest to define the indefinable something we all obviously seek. The operative word is *unsuccessful*. If any of the learned tomes had actually delivered the hot scoops their jackets promised, you would be doing something more worthwhile at the moment than plowing into number 842,606. Well, wouldn't you?

Forewarned is forearmed. The magic something isn't here either. No guarantees of any kind, for that matter. Just a few ideas, tips, hunches, dirty tricks, and even some facts designed to make the search more fun. Their source is the ultimate authority: you. Their goal is the answer to one simple question. If, as most of the card-carrying sages over the centuries have said, "Life is either a problem or a privilege," how can we learn to opt for number two?

We are in this transient mess together, so let's try to find out. We won't cure each other's spastic colons, diaphragmatic hernias, migraines, or the rest of our collective bag of psychosomatic gaggles. But as Mickey Rooney must certainly have intended on one or more of his wind sprints up the aisle, we may be able to make it borderline bearable. That is the plan. We shall start at the start and almost never look back. We have based this uncharacteristically logical game plan on the probability that we couldn't do the latter if we tried. I mean, how much backtracking can you really expect to be able to cram into fifteen ten-thousandths of a second?

Fifteen ten-thousandths of a second is about as long as it takes a reasonably healthy hummingbird to work up one good flap of its wings. According to one of those great-looking, not to mention terrifically pointless, charts that always fall out of 1957 *National*

Geographics when you accidentally open hall closets, it will also be pretty close to the extent of your total contribution to the big picture. Seems that a few of the *Geographic*'s editors, who were evidently between assignments to exotic places where naked women do not wear staples in their navels, got together one day and decided to help the rest of us get a handle on the 4.5-billion-year history of our planet. Guessing correctly that the notion of 4.5 billion years or 4.5 billion anything elses was downright boggling, they condensed and simplified the history of the world to the equivalent of one day. To simplify that simplification, look at the face of an old clock and pretend it represents 4.5 billion years instead of 24 hours. It must, for this exciting experiment to succeed, be an old clock because new clocks do not have faces. They have computerized digital readout panels, which do not translate well to histories of the world. Neither did Mel Brooks's sense of humor, but that is another matter.

Anyway, on that kind of scale an hour would equal roughly 180 million years. A single minute would last about 3 million years. One quick second would roll for 50,000 years and so on. A lifetime? You guessed it; fifteen ten-thousandths of a second. Scary, huh?

No, not really. The exercise is merely a hypothetical comparison with very little relevance to anyone except, perhaps, Carl Sagan, who does not count because he comes from Vega or some such barely discovered galaxy billions and billions of light-years away, where people or whatever they call themselves live billions and billions of years without ever having to pretend they enjoy yogurt or ballet. As the title suggests, most of us less fortunates would actually have seventy-some earth years in which to figure it all out if we played our cards right. Catch is, most of us will not do that. Instead, we shall convince ourselves that the rules apply only to all those other schlumps. We shall puff away a few minutes here and munch away a **few** minutes there and generally have us a good ol' time. Then, when the factory warranty is just about to run out, we'll change our minds and decide to go straight. After a bypass or two.

That's called human nature.

That's also called flunking social studies, which is contemporary jargon for history full of famous and infamous folks who apparently thought the same way. As if their misadventures were not proof enough of our guaranteed mortality, we get constant reminders from those absolute self-professed experts on almost everything, the insurance companies. They can peg your demise to the minute. They not only can but do. How else do you suppose they wind up having all of those big buildings and golf tournaments named after them?

Like to know how they do it? Once again you have come to the right place. The formula is in the chapter between the one about how to get a key to the executive john and the one about how to survive midlife crisis once you have got a key to the executive john. Match its projections to your secret life-style, and you may well be the first on your block to be able to predict your very own death date just as such morbid notables as Old Blue Eyes, Carnac the Magnificent, and Henry the K, among others, already have. You will no doubt also be the last on your block to do anything constructive to change it.

That's called freedom of choice. It means that we all get first dibs on how to play out our precious flap in the sun. We can live it up and face the music quickly, or we can get our acts together and, seeming contradiction notwithstanding, enjoy the long run. Either way we had best get moving before another ice age sneaks up on us. If my watch is correct, the next one is due in about forty-three seconds. Have your thermal mittens ready.

ONE:

Those Good Old Young Days

1

Age: 0 to 0.6

Talk about postnatal depression, for fifteen or twenty crazy seconds there you have the world on an umbilical cord. Then some sour grape comes along and messes up everything with one vindictive snip of a surgical scissor. As you soon learn, that rude shock to your system is but the first in a lifelong series of unsolicited lessons which will fall under the categorical heading "reality."

Lesson 2: Complete strangers are going to be snipping at your cords and various other more or less vital parts from here on out.

Lesson 3: What's done is done. Not all the king's horses or all the king's men will ever tie you back to the mother ship again.

Lesson 4: You are on your own. Review your options as they tumble into place, and adjust. Whatever you do, adjust!

Anyway, for better or probably worse, here you are—all prunylooking and ready to roll. Now what? Simple, enjoy! For the moment you are a jillionaire. Adoring slaves are going to carry you on pillows of satin. They will jump at your slightest grunt, prepare wondrous potions only for your lips, and whisper soothing incantations in your honor all day and, if you play it right, all night long. Life is a piece of cake. Okay, since you do not have any teeth yet, it is a slurp of cake. Let's not get all hung up on details. There will be plenty of time for that later.

The first rule of a successful infancy is not to start feeling guilty about getting the royal treatment. Plenty of time for that later as well. Besides, what reason is there for a guilt trip? Did you ask for this assignment? Did you volunteer to spend the better part of a year bobbing in a pitch-black dunk tank only to have someone yank you out and start slapping you around just when you were getting the hang of it? Of course not, loosen up! This whole thing was someone else's idea (someone else's fault anyway), and you're the one who is going to have to live with it. That will not always be so easy. Like it or not, your lease on the lap of luxury is temporary. You will be doing the jumping and cootchy-cooing yourself before long. Make the most of fat city while you can.

Second, squirm a lot. Big people get nervous if you ever look too comfortable. Then they start poking you and shaking the bed and doing all sorts of unpleasant things. If you're going to get bounced around anyhow, you may as well call the shots. The experience will come in handy when you begin your basic assertiveness training in Little League.

Third, develop a sense of humor. You'll need one. Adults, especially the kinds with whiskers and bellies that do not fit into belts, are usually well intentioned and utterly inept with people your size. They exaggerate your fragility and expect to kill you accidentally at any minute. The only way to keep your sanity is to put them on every once in a while. You will obviously have to experiment to find the material that best suits your individual talents, but here are a few idea-starter routines that have played well for others over the generations:

Hold your breath. It never fails to get a rise.

Grab your soft spot, and scream. Another guaranteed show stopper.

Gagging and turning blue are usually good.

Twist your elbow backward while crossing your eyes. They won't know what to panic about first.

Choose something like *inextricably* or *eleemosynary* for your first word. Once your parents get over the shock and start bragging about their budding Mensa, hit the neighbors with *dada* and *goo*.

Best of all, rip off and hide the tip of your pacifier. Then gag hysterically. It will drive the old folks right up the nearest wall.

Fourth, work on your timing. You may never have more or better opportunities to hone this crucial skill than you have right now. Make the most of them.

Be sure, for example, to take advantage of diaper changes for precision peeing practice. Unless an unexpected target of opportunity as appealing as your mother's new hairdo presents itself, aim for the nose. A couple of degrees off target in any direction will still get the job done. Incidentally, the fact that this particular drill is so much tougher for girls than boys may explain the penis envy routine, which is supposedly rampant among the former until they reach the age at which they can tell the latter what to do with their supposedly envied appendages. An interesting, albeit anatomically impossible experiment. Not at all what the boys will have in mind at that particular stage of their development.

Catch all that? This child psychology is tricky stuff. Takes all kinds of dependent clauses to explain it poorly, and even then there are no assurances it will work. Ask Peter Pan. Better yet, ask Dr. Dan Kiley, author of *The Peter Pan Syndrome*. Best of all, ask his wife.

To get the most from your frequent vomiting sessions, try not to spit up when Dad is wearing his favorite high school sweat shirt with the holes in the elbows. Wait for a clean shot at his cashmere or three-piece from Burberry's.

If your parents return at two-thirty in the morning from their first night out since you joined the team, give them a break. Don't start bawling until three or so, by which point they may be doing the same thing, sort of. Don't stop until eight. Sleep angelically all day.

Stop coughing when you reach the doctor's office. Start hacking again, more violently than ever, as soon as you get back to the car. Repeat as opportunities allow.

When you know that Grandma is coming to visit, pull a blanket over your face and develop a rash. Grandmas love having things like that to notice and mention casually to regular mas. This is especially effective if it is your daddy's mommy who is doing the visiting. It will give her and your own mom something to talk about. You would be surprised by what terrific conversations mothers and grandmothers can have once you get them going.

Scream bloody murder the moment you and Grandpa are alone in a room together. Continue until Grandma comes to the rescue. She is capable of having some really interesting conversations with Grandpa as well.

Fifth, don't be shy. The meek may eventually inherit the earth and all, but I don't believe that I would suggest holding your breath in anticipation of the big event. If you want something, you have to go for it. And you can never start too soon. In case you hadn't noticed, neither of us is getting any younger.

Sixth, get religion. Any religion. Without one, you may not know how to be firm in your positions regarding important social issues such as whether or not half of the people in the world should be in charge of their bodies. As a bonus, religions usually have excellent insurance policies and are relatively painless to join unless you happen to be a boy. (Contrary to general *goy* belief, not all Jewish children are circumcised.) Basically, all you have to do is get through a tricky little ceremony during which you get dunked, salted, and oiled by a nice man in a dress and, probably because of all the dunking/salting/oiling, nicknamed Peanuts by some terribly original male relative whose primary role as your honorary godfather is to disappear immediately and permanently.

Seventh, regardless of what they may think the nice man in the fancy dress has thereby officially named you, absolutely refuse to react in any way to wimpy-sounding identifiers like Waldo, Abigail, or Moon Unit. Well, Moon Unit may be okay. I mean, like gag me with a spoon, it worked like totally the most for Frank Zappa's kid. Forget the rest, though. Names chase you through life. In fact, they precede you.

Get stuck with one that doesn't fit, and you will have some problems. Brewski chugalugging bleacher bums seldom get rabid over jocks named Roscoe. Neither lascivious nor liberated, Maude and Yolanda offer the worst of both worlds. Harley, Bertha, Elmo, and Emmett all are guaranteed losers as well. How are you supposed to strut in and close a big deal with some mogul who thinks your calling card is the funniest thing she has ever seen? This is a serious situation. Address it immediately. Take action. Don't under any circumstances, including severe tickling or the offer of applesauce instead of spinach for lunch, giggle lovably at them until they call you something acceptable. If it worked for a guy with the unlikely moniker Pavlov, it can work for you.

This is not to imply that you are automatically out of the woods even if you happen to catch a good one like the current favorite: Michael. If your dad was in the mood to stretch for a little immortality at the time, he might have named you after himself, in which case you would be Michael, Jr. If his dad had the same unfortunate notion, you would be Michael III. Carry the pattern out to obscene extreme, and some poor mope is going to be walking around a couple of hundred years from now trying to explain a driver's license that reads Michael XII. Of course, by then, computerized den mothers and other authority figures may not be programmed to recognize people named Joe or Fred anyway. Tell you what, forget about this whole name business. It isn't worth the hassle. Let them call you whatever they choose. When you grow up, you can always change it to Moon Unit on your own.

Eighth, take it slow. From here on in, it's going to be all downhill.

Wondering what, if anything, all this prepubescent burbling has to do with someone old enough to read? Fair question. Frankly, not much this time around, but it should come in handy when you apply for your next reincarnation permit. Might even convince you to transmigrate as something more logical and promising than a human. I, for one, am currently rather high on the notion of coming back as a French poodle or Lhasa Apso confidant of some Park Avenue dowager whose chauffeur's main assignment would be keeping the Rolls running during my pit stops in Central Park and cubing my chateaubriand. Then again, I might just decide to be something unpretentious like a bar of soap in Christie Brinkley's shower.

This has admittedly been a lot for you to digest. But then digesting is what you do best at the moment, so everything ought to come out all right.

2
Age: 0.6 to 6.0

Bed wetters, beware. At the very least, pay attention. This "Sesame Street" phase is important. It teaches the difference between good and evil and, thanks to that omnipresent role model and fashion plate Mr. Rogers, proves that burglars are not the only ones who wear sneakers around the house. Unfortunately, what with delivering your first doses of reward and punishment and setting the hook for lifetime supplies of bad habits, prejudices, and sexual hang-ups, it can also be something of a bummer.

The big guys' attitude switch was probably your first hint of things to come. Whereas until a couple of weeks ago everyone seemed to think you were about the cutest thing since Polaroid commercials, now it is as though they were bugged because you don't have a job yet. Life is becoming one crisis after another, and their pat answer to every one of them is "nap time."

Remember how meals used to be wet, sweet adventures full of hugging and kissing? No more. Not even close. Mom's lap and other even nicer parts have been replaced by a distinctly precarious contraption with a school desk top that snaps menacingly against your belly. Significantly understating the case, they call it a high chair. To someone your size the damn thing looks like the Eiffel Tower. Especially when you are up there in its observation deck without a parachute. This impression is compounded by horror stories they have been telling you lately about egg-shaped creatures and little kids who fall down and shatter into zillions of pieces.

As if having to hang on for dear life way up there isn't harrowing enough, you have probably also noticed that they are trying to poison you. No sooner are you clamped in place than they start shoveling gravelly-tasting mush in your general direction and forcing you to swallow. What's worse, they insult your intelligence by rolling their eyes, smacking their lips, and pretending to love alternate spoonfuls themselves. If you survive long enough, you will learn a word or two for the way they are acting. On the other hand, you may get lucky and grow up illiterate.

Suddenly there are rules for or, to be more accurate, against almost everything. Drooling on furniture and knocking over potted plants are definite no-no's. Checking out light sockets, eating shoe polish, and pulling the dog's whiskers are international incidents punishable by immediate confinement to a cockamamie swing sort of deal that dingles you into blithering submission with off-key renditions of such favorites as "London Bridge Is Falling Down" and the ever-intimidating "Pop Goes the Weasel." Catch any pattern here? Right: Be good, or they'll drop you, pop you, and who knows what all, up to and including calling in the boogeyman to play the heavy. Really big trouble calls for a particularly unpleasant indignity which is usually preceded by a really dumb line like "Now this is going to hurt me more than it will hurt you." When applied to small people, it is called spanking. Between consenting adults, it is called foreplay. Some adults have odd ideas about how to play. In any event, the experience is guaranteed to make the high chair routine even harder to take.

All this is small potatoes compared to the real kick they are now on. It is a world-class beaut called potty training. As the name implies, the basic prop is the potty—a cold, little plastic chair with a hole in the middle. The trick, near as you can probably tell from available information, is to sit on it for several hours at a crack. All the while you will be encouraged to do everything except what you will eventually, no doubt accidentally, discover you are actually expected to, uh, do. No, I don't know why people so often seem to be trying to teach you one thing while hammering home quite another. Like pastel wallpaper and bunnies in the nursery, that is just the way it is. One of life's important mysteries, I suppose. Take the case in point. For openers, "Make number two" has very little to do with arithmetic. Nor, for that matter, do all the other cutesy euphemisms. The idea is to get some natural functions in line with sanitary necessity and social custom. So what is the big *gedilleh*? If they have something on their minds, why don't they simply say so? Such nonsense is unnecessarily confusing and potentially dangerous. The way in which you survive the ordeal of seeing a part of yourself, even an icky part, get tossed down the chutes will dictate the approach you take to an awful lot of what lies ahead.

Do it wrong, and you will be an undesirable bridge partner for life. Get to enjoying yourself too much, and you may grow up to be a proctologist. You would then develop a new appreciation for the term *the absolute pits* and be in for a cradle-to-grave barrage of tight-end jokes. Pledge time: When you get around to being one of the big guys, give your own kids a break. Lay tile and buy a mop.

In the meanwhile, stay calm. One of two things will happen. You will survive or you won't. If the former, one more thing will happen. Sex! Or, as some folks might refer to it, ₛₑₓ. Lots of luck if you happened to have drawn members of the latter crowd in the parent lottery. Whether your ancestors care to admit it or not, sex very probably had a little something to do with your arrival. It is natural, wholesome, necessary, and, most important, big biz. In fact, many advertising executives and other renowned financial experts say it is one of the foundation stones of our nation's entire economy—right up there with pet food, illicit Bolivian plant life, and "Monday Night Football." If you don't believe it, check what happened to maternity wards and, not coincidentally, the stock market nine months after the NFL strike.

Fact of life: The three Rs look good on what used to be called report cards, but the three Bs sell soap. They also sell airplane rides and toothpaste and beer and cars and everything else. So if Aunt Edna ever catches you and your cousin playing doctor, tell her you are being patriotic. Who knows? You may even get away with it.

That is also in the great American tradition. Getting away with things is, in fact, the stuff of legends. Without a bit of assiduous shuffling and jiving, Mark Twain, for example, might have remained Samuel Clemens. Hannibal, Missouri, would then have been left without a tourist trade. That, in turn, would have undermined the celebrity status of the mighty Mississippi and given New Yorkers even more cause to wonder aloud about the existence of anything west of their own muddy river. Since there is no way they could survive the resultant ego overload, there would be no one available to spill the garbage of one of the world's great cities, act rudely, or charge $53 for breakfast. Without the big sting, the Big Apple would be in big trouble. If you find that you have what it takes, be a con artist. It is your duty. In the long run, Aunt Edna will be proud.

No need to hurry things by hanging out with undesirables, though. You can get all the positive role modeling you will need for a while from a terrific educational tool right in the privacy of your very own home. If you are similar to most kids, you spend twenty-seven and a half hours a day staring at the beast. Unless you are trying to cut down, in which case a steady diet of Richard Simmons shows is suggested, you might as well get something out of it.

Plenty there to get. Television has more than enough sex and bunco lessons to start you off on the right wrong foot. Almost nothing else, in fact, unless you count the important commercial messages that pop up every ten or fifteen seconds. Featuring casts of thousands and all kinds of exotic camera angles and computer graphics, these minimasterpieces often cost more to produce than the programs they mercifully interrupt. Their role is to share socially relevant information concerning socially relevant things made by socially relevant Japanese conglomerates that would like to have you get all excited and make your parents immediately run out to buy some. Come to think of it, even the ads usually star more attractively bulgy types and smooth talkers dressed in what used to be called risqué attire than anything else. Must be why they still call it the boob tube just the way they used to.

None of this is really likely to ring your bells for a while anyway. As soon as you start to get the hang of this sex deal, involuntary hiatus is going to set in for a few years. No one ever said it was going to be one long bed of posies, pal. In later life this unfortunate malady will be known as impotence or frigidity depending upon your gender. Today it is called the terrible twos regardless of team affiliation. Hard to figure why. Two is actually pretty excellent.

By two you can climb, nurture sibling rivalries, and have all kinds of other outstanding adventures. There are puppies to love. Sandboxes. Twinkies. Running. Mud. About 40,000 kinds of plastic creatures to do your playing for you. Grass. (No, not that kind of grass. Don't be so precocious.) Butterflies. Dr. Seuss. More running. Falling down. Potato chips. Blocks. Trucks. Dolls. Pudding. Grandparents. Kids next door. The hairs on your father's chest. Pots and pans and, if you luck out and your parents do not, a baby brother or sister to bonk accidentally whenever no one is looking. There are also droopy drawers and measles shots, but on the whole, life is good. The world is out there to explore and enjoy.

Do that. And do it for real. These formative years are too crucial to your future development to blow on anything less than all-out effort. Like it or not, you will be you by the time you are six years old. Your character will be formed; your neuroses entrenched (oops, neurosis is a term no longer in general use. This is primarily because no one could ever spell it correctly; *disorder* is now the big favorite. Either way the reference is to women who are sorry the morning after whether they did or did not the night before), your career and assorted off-hours preferences determined. Straight scoop: By six the entire script is written. All that will be left for you to do thereafter is to play it all out. Pay attention. You can tell an awful lot about what you will be by noticing what you are, what you enjoy, what you do.

If, for example, your current tastes and aptitudes seem to fall in the column on the lower left, your future comings and goings will probably lean distinctly right. Congratulations or condolences as the combinations will make eventually appropriate.

Juvenile Propensities	Adult Probabilities
Excel at exciting, chancy games, such as marbles and pitching pennies?	You will no doubt grow up to be a Vegas dealer or demolition derby champ.
Prefer blocks, Busy Boxes and similarly docile activities?	Terrific! CPAs and English teachers will always be in demand. Dull, but in demand.
Double-jump your thing?	You are a born barrister. If you also happen to have difficulty forming simple Anglo-Saxon sentences, you will carry the profession to its highest level and become a politician.
Skateboard enthusiast?	The right stuff is there for future shuttle missions. Also for future insurance claim swindles. So what do you think? Want to be respected or rich?
Mud pie specialist?	Always popular. Probably explains why there are so many beauticians, geologists, and newspaper columnists running around.
Mumbletypeg master?	Antiques dealer. No contest.
Enjoy coloring?	As an adult you will enjoy coloring. Some things never change.
Enjoy playing doctor even more?	You will be wealthy and oversexed.
Build snowmen all winter long?	You are a budding chauvinist pig. Dumb, too. Snowwomen are easier.
Build them all year long?	You are either an Eskimo or a bit flaky, but you may make it as a magician's rabbit or hockey puck.
Like to dress up in your mommy's old clothes?	You will be a fashion model or closet transvestite or both.
Cops and robbers?	You will be a law enforcement officer or barn boss or both.
Ambidextrous?	That's nice. Useless, but nice.

This junior prophet patrol number works with other current activities and preferences as well. Food, for continued instance.

If Your All-Time Favorites Include . . .	You Will No Doubt Be . . .
Big Macs	Very typical.
Quiche	A pro football linebacker. That other book has it all wrong. Real women are the ones who don't eat quiche. They prefer tartar steak with lots of onions and a shooter on the side. Lib, y'know.
Chicken soup	Healthy and a lifelong momma's boy.
Fish	Smart.
Sweetbreads	Brave.
Jelly beans	A grade B movie actor or a grade B chief executive or both.
Oatmeal	Strong.
Carrots	Skinny.
Éclairs	Fat.
Sugar	Pimply, and your dentist's favorite.
Vegetables	A protester.

Let us not forget such cerebral pursuits as . . .

Reading	Portentous of extremely nonconformist attitudes to come.
Writing	Maladjusted, probably alcoholic.
Mathematical curiosity	Not much of a freethinker, are you?
Computer skills	Anything you care to be. Those who are on first-name bases with computers will rule the world by next Tuesday.

Have any idols?

Snoopy	You will be a World War III flying ace. This promises to be a very glamorous, very short career.
Garfield	Basic run-of-the-mill smart ass.
Doonesbury	Member of the Rand think tank
Dr. Seuss	Poet, shuttle diplomat, or person who enjoys funny-looking food.
Moe, Larry, Curly	Punch-drunk.
J. Theisman	photogenic.
C. Brinkley	PHOTOGENIC.
R. Kittle	Handsome, but an ugly winner.
L. Skywalker	A definite Force.
D. Bowie	Confused.
M. Navratilova	Invincible.
A. E. Newman	A guest host on "SNL."
Mr. T	Anything you care to be.
C. Eastwood	Dirty, hairy.
T. Koppel	Haggard-looking. Staying up that late gives you bags. Of course, it also confers terrific credibility.
M. Jackson	Thrilling.
K. Jackson	Angelic.
R. Jackson	More so.
M. Streep	Statuesque.
S. Spielberg	Extraterrestrial.
G. Burns	Optimistic.
W. Allen	A Yuppie.
E.T.	A homebody.
Orphan Annie	Irritating.
ABBA	Abbookkeeper.

Your thundering threes, frantic fours, and forgetful fives will also be chock-full of ominous portents of things to come. Be sure to keep an eye open. For that matter, keep both eyes open. This ability to look back at tomorrow is very rare—unprecedented, in fact. Whereas your generation can actually see what is behind the beyond, its predecessors have had trouble getting much beyond the behind. If you do not like what you see, you surely won't care for what you get.

One last piece of advice before it is too late: Watch the old folks. They don't have to be named Oedipus or Electra to be complex enough influences to leave you a total wreck before they're through. If you are not very careful, you may wind up more similar to them than they to you, in which case they may do the same. You would then be dependent upon a couple of selfish little kids for all your worldly needs until you could provide for yourself, a time that may be never. Of course, it's confusing. Confusing is precisely what it is supposed to be at this all-important formative stage.

These harrowing experiences of youth are scientifically designed both to give parents something to do and to create the cuckoos of tomorrow without whom latter-day Jungs and Adlers would have to get real jobs. The frightened child in the wobbly high chair today is the white-knuckles mope they'll be strapping into 797 no-snorting sections sometime next century. The victim of today's boogeyman will be the harried possessor of tomorrow's phobias. This is where it all begins. Lots of luck. You may need it. Psychobabblists everywhere are counting on you.

3

Age: 6 to ?
(Your Days Are
Numbered)

Like it or not, you are now officially set: set in your ways; set in your attitudes; set in your approach to almost everything you will ever do or think or be. For better or for worse, by six you are you. From here on out you will spend most of your time trying to figure out who that is. Success or failure in this noble quest will probably depend upon how much time you have left to figure out how much time you have left to do the rest of your figuring.

Believe it or not, you can. (In fact, if you survived the last sentence of the last paragraph, you can do anything.) The insurance industry's more or less actuarially accurate life-style pop quiz follows. Take it at your own risk, and you will be able to predict the date of your very own demise. Fun idea, huh? Here's how it works. Scribble your projected maximum allotment (75 years should be close enough for openers) on the margin of any handy high-fiber cereal box or the margin of this page, and add or deduct a few years here and there as appropriate to your likely future habits.

If you are male, subtract 3 years right off the top.
If you are female, add 4.5 years (and feel legitimately superior).
Are you intense, aggressive, easily angered? Subtract 3.
Easygoing and relaxed? Add 3.

Are you basically happy? Add 1.
Unhappy? Subtract 2.
Have you had a speeding ticket within the last year? Subtract 1.
Do you smoke more than two packs a day? Subtract 8.
One to two packs? Subtract 6.
One-half to one? Subtract 3.
Do you drink the equivalent of 1½ ounces of liquor per day?
Subtract 1.
Twelve or more soft drinks a day? Subtract 2.
Are you overweight by 50 pounds or more? Subtract 8.
By 30 to 50? Subtract 4.
By 10 to 30. Subtract 2.
If you are a man over 40 and have an annual checkup, add 2.
If you are a woman and see a gynecologist once a year, add 2.
(Once a month? Have fun.)
Are you a housewife or working mother? Go directly to heaven!

Now, if you have stayed awake and done all the math properly, you are entirely capable of predicting your precise death date. Doesn't that give you a terrific feeling of accomplishment? It should. You have joined a select club of farsighted luminaries which boasts the memberships of Johnny Carson, who will keel over on January 26, 2005; Mr. Sinatra, who will do so on September 14, 1998; and Barbra Streisand, who will remain the possessor of the most perfect pipes you will ever hear and a nose until December 25, 2024. Hope that didn't come as a surprise to any of them. You don't suppose they really bought that immortality stuff, do you? Oops. Almost forgot Henry Kissinger. I'm not sure of him because I do not know when we're going to run out of Republican presidents. I'm sure he wouldn't think of leaving while still being needed to help save the world or give private diction lessons.

TWO:
The Awkward Stage

(Somewhere Between Puberty and Tummy Tucks)

When the Free Ride Ends

You are about to have your faith in human nature and concept of how the world works severely shaken. One day soon you will roll out of the sack at eleven or so, just as you always have. You will stroll down to devastate the refrigerator casually, just as you always have. You will trip over the dog and flip a sarcastic shot at your nearest available sibling, just as you always have. So far so good, but hardly far enough. As you reach for your minimum daily overdose of sugared preservatives, you will notice that something is different—different and somehow very wrong. Someone with a warped sense of humor will have opened the morning paper not to the comforting wisdom of "The Far Side" or last night's crucial curling scores, but to the—gasp and shudder—employment opportunities section. What's worse, several particularly odious ads will be circled in red.

Just like that, those loving souls who have nurtured you, supported you, reinforced, educated, and generally fawned all over you since day one will have done a psychological 180 and suggested that you perform an unnatural act, one that will change your already perfectly acceptable life-style forever. They will have recommended—no, make that "demanded"—that you get a job. This is no laughing matter. It is reality time, and to use the most recently outdated *au courant* vernacular, it sucks.

You will immediately begin a classic pattern of emotional response. An initial flush of disoriented rage will bleed—and I do mean bleed—quickly into a cooler state of quiet denial. Equally unpleasant periods of thoroughly ineffective bargaining, prolonged depression, and finally, inevitably, acceptance will follow. This is normal and, unless you are blessed with uncommon courage of conviction or inordinate fondness for poverty, irresistible. There is no sense trying to fight it. Once the shock and horror wear off, you will decide to go along with their plan. The speed with which you decide to do so will be in direct proportion to the speed with which you realize that they are seriously considering cutting off your groceries.

Fact of life: The prospect of imminent starvation alters one's perspective.

Do not panic. People have been receiving and surviving such bulletins for centuries. Many have even gotten to the point of actually enjoying having to do something for a living. With luck you will not be one of them, but it couldn't hurt to review your options carefully and make the correct call just in case. Right or wrong, your choice of vocation will define your role and your image and your wardrobe and your almost everything else for the next fifty or sixty years. No sense stifling the heart and soul of a perfectly good cosmetician in the shell of a computer programmer. There is nothing worse than being stuck in a job that does not fit. Take Lee Iacocca. The man could have been a really adequate junior high school principal had he not been drafted as a common commercial pitchman, corporate savior, and mystery guest on bimonthly Bob Hope specials.

Some careers pay enormous salaries and put holes in stomach linings. Others turn the balance of payments around and produce reasonably well-adjusted paupers. Still others are heavy on the promise of such ephemeral carrots as status, fulfillment, relevance, and, best of all, groupie appeal. Your alternatives are endless. The trick to sliding in the single best direction for your unique abilities and drives is knowing what you really want most in return for all your trouble.

Prestige your thing? On the basis of such positively perceived character traits as respectability and trustworthiness, surveys of general attitude have historically ranked high-profile professionals whom people believe (most believable to least) about as follows:

1. Physicians
2. Clergymen
3. Dentists
4. Judges
5. Psychologists
6. College professors
7. Psychiatrists
8. High school teachers
9. Lawyers
10. Law enforcement officials
11. TV news reporters
12. Plumbers
13. Executives of large corporations
14. U.S. Army generals
15. TV repairmen
16. Newspaper columnists
17. Auto repairmen
18. Labor union officials
19. Politicians
20. Used car salesmen

Nothing very surprising in that, unless you get to wondering why newspaper columnists and politicians are considered more trustworthy than used car salesmen. No explaining surveys of general attitude, I guess.

Good times sound more like what you have in mind? Dream jobs vary widely from one mindset to another, but consensus winners usually include centerfold photographers, professional shoppers, fashion models, ski instructors, sports color commentators, tasters in junk food factories, singles-bar tenders, single bartenders, and rodeo clowns. Dogcatchers, bill collectors, door-to-door Bible peddlers, human guinea pigs, slaughterhouse hammermen, and

incinerators for the U.S. Mint normally do not fare quite as well.
On the other hand, they are not too tough to get, so you may want
to jot some notes in case you are devoid of featherbedding
qualifications.
Never quite got over Haight-Ashbury, nonconformity, and otherwise hyphenated hang-up days? Do not, under any circum-
stance, sign on as a secretary, steno, teacher, or retail sales type.
They are America's most common jobs. Others in this yawn and
trudge category include truck drivers, private-household workers,
and white-collar whatevers. For some real exclusivity, try your
hand at sponge diving. At last count, there were exactly twelve of
them splashing around on a full-time basis.
     Into excitement and danger? Again, spongers top the list of
emulatable daredevils. Bet you never realized the profession was
such a big deal. Neither did they. When someone recently told
one of them about their unique role in society, he responded,
"Oh, yeah. No kidding? Huh! Wanna buy a sponge?" Hey, you
gotta make a living. As do such other surefire achievers of harrowing adventure like Green Berets, red berets, puce berets, motorcy-
cle racers, stunt people, aerialists, rattlesnake milkers, coal miners,
nuclear reactor maintenance engineers, test drivers and pilots,
spies, steel mill hookers, middle linebackers, the other kind of
hookers, electrical pole people, fisher people, lumberjacks, cops,
and presidents of the United States. To explain that another way,
people who hold such jobs tend to get hurt and/or killed while at
work way more often than average mopes. Dentists, for example,
hardly ever get involuntarily killed on the job. That may explain
their ridiculously high suicide rate. Then again, it may not.
     Need the emotional security blanket of bright future promise?
Money magazine has devised a rating system with which its editors
sort out the professions that hold the most and least employment
promise in coming years. Its most recent upside selections were
doctor, veterinarian, systems analyst, dentist, geologist, actuary,
personnel administrator, city manager, engineer, and pharmacist.
Those with the worst prospects (for purpose of the rating system,
prospects are defined as things like promotions, opportunities, sal-

ary, supply, and demand) are schoolteacher, librarian, clergy, forester, newspaper reporter, hotel manager, college prof, military officer, biologist and, would you believe, lawyer. How's that for happy news!

Still feeling insecure? *U.S. News & World Report* says these will be the top jobs come the turn of the century:

Telemarketing workers
CAD/CAM (computers)
Software writers
Geriatric social workers
Housing rehabilitation workers
Energy conservation specialists
Emergency medical technicians
Gerontological aides
Hazardous-waste technicians
Energy auditors
Battery technicians
Technical aides for the handicapped
Emission technologists
Radiation therapists
Respiratory therapists
Biomedical and electronic technicians
Nuclear medical technicians
Industrial hygiene technicians
Bionic implant technicians
Dialysis technicians

Sounds as if we all have dandy futures ahead. Wonder whatever became of cowboys and firemen and beauty pageant contestants?

Big bucks at any cost? No contest. Be Paul McCartney. You will earn $50 million a year, give or take a million (believe it breaks down to five grand an hour), and be allowed to carry suitcases full of marijuana into foreign countries without being invited to visit foreign prisons for the rest of your life. This is a good deal.

Far better than most non-Paul McCartneys with suitcases or fake heels or body cavities or whatevers full of marijuana usually get when visiting foreign countries. Especially Turkey.

So, for that matter, are the perks of lesser superstar billing. Bob Hope, Gene Autry, Steve Allen, Francis Albert Sinatra, Lucille Ball, Stuart Whitman, Lawrence Welk, Art Linkletter, Herb Alpert, Roy Rogers, Fred MacMurray, Mick Jagger, and the rest of the surviving Beatles all are rumored to have estates in the half-billion-dollar range. Even Marlon ("I don't want your Oscar, but I've asked this Indian princess to make a socially relevant speech on my behalf anyway") Brando, Alan ("M*A*S*H"/Lib/Atari) Alda, Bill (pea soup makes the best vomit) Friedkin, Jane ("Gimme a cause, any cause" née Barbarella Goodbody) Fonda, Steven ("Some of my best friends are short") Spielberg, George ("Box office is my middle name") Lucas, and Michael (Wanna trade noses?) Jackson are apparently able to scratch by on their measly 100 million or so. No, come to think of it, Michael's Victory Tour probably moved him up a notch or two.

"Roar of the greasepaint and smell of the crowd" leave your bells unrung? Do something else, perhaps something in a nice floundering multinational conglomerate. It will not matter if you are any good at boardroom intrigue or other big biz skills as long as you can hang in long enough to weave yourself a golden parachute for a rainy day. To do that, simply get an Ivy League M.B.A. or strike up a close personal relationship with some good-looking corporate strategic planner who happens to have one.

Yet another potentially lucrative option is being selected to dictate some small country with unlimited oil reserves. As Anne Bancroft's husband once said, "It's good to be da king."

Worse comes to worst, you can always invent something everyone else has always thought of inventing or become a world-class crook.

Although income estimates for potentates, inventors, and most bad guys who are any good are tough to come by, a couple of snoops named David Harrop and Roy Blount, Jr., were able to dig up enough other biggies' W-2s to fill several of *Playboy*'s socially redeeming pages not long ago. For purposes of comparison, they also threw in a few working stiffs, took a wide cross section of gross annual incomes, and broke them down to the equivalent of hourly wages. On the off-chance you did not make it past the cartoons that month, here is what they found:

Job or Person	Hourly Rate in Dollars
Bus driver (San Francisco)	10.09
Dave Winfield	721.15
(outfielder, New York Yankees)	
General-duty nurse	5.93
George Shultz	33.47
(secretary of state)	
Plumber (Seattle)	16.71
David Stockman	33.47
(director, Office of Management and Budget)	
Musician	13.25
(New York Philharmonic)	
Architect	16.82
Barber	7.50
NBA player (average)	104.80
Wayne Newton	5,769.23
(for Vegas shows only)	
Bank teller	4.90
Donald C. Platten	370.19
(chairman, Chemical New York Corporation [bank])	
John J. O'Donnell	52.00
(president, Air Line Pilots International Association)	
Shoe repairman	6.25
Lady Pink	20.00
(New York graffiti artist-superstar)	
High-fashion model (average)	26.44
Truck driver (Chicago)	11.56
Tom Brokaw	721.00
(TV journalist)	
Word processing operator	7.69
Corrections officer	7.71
(Alabama prison guard)	
Social worker	6.34
C. C. Garvin	483.65
(president, EXXON)	
Bartender (Washington, D.C.)	5.26
Drug pusher	72.11
(estimated when successful)	

Job or Person	Hourly Rate in Dollars
Senior editor (Time magazine)	33.65
Resident M.D. (first year)	7.59
William Ruckelshaus	33.47
(former secretary of the interior)	
Flight attendant	11.79
(Eastern Airlines, top salary)	
Jackie Sherrill	137.98
(football coach, Texas A&M)	
Parachute packer (nongolden)	8.76
Private, first class, U.S. Army	3.81
Insurance agent	19.23
Reporter (major city)	14.00
Lee Iacocca	174.03
(chairman, Chrysler Corporation)	
Dentist (net)	31.25
Bowling equipment repairman	9.06
Funeral director (federal job)	13.94
Chiropractor	15.38
David Brinkley	360.57
(TV journalist)	
Pharmacist	16.44
(senior staff)	
Janitor (Denver)	6.26
Supermarket cashier	7.53
Auctioneer	21.63
Author (average)	2.29
Call girl (independent)	60.00
General John J. Vessey, Jr.	27.64
(chairman, Joint Chiefs)	
State policeman (Texas)	8.29
Steelworker (roller)	12.35
Auto assembly-line painter	9.91
Locomotive engineer	14.86
Director of data processing	17.34
Jim Palmer	300.48
(pitcher-underwear model)	
Screenwriter (successful)	25.31
Petroleum engineer	18.02
Messenger	4.10
Gary Coleman	288.46
Travel agency manager	9.13
Trustee (Duke endowed)	30.64
Educational Testing Service Director	42.30
Tugboat operator	8.12

Lane Kirkland	52.88
(president, AFL-CIO)	
IRS agent (average)	10.81
Hotel Cook (Detroit)	5.06
TV network researcher	10.31
Real estate agent (average, full-time)	8.65
Dolls, games, toys manufacturing worker	5.56
John McEnroe (tennis only)	476.44
Security guard (Dallas)	6.85
Psychiatrist	27.88
Juggler	9.37
Priest	1.73
Partner (major law firm)	92.93
Professor (University of Maine)	13.89
Secret Service Agent (average)	9.01
Bank robber (successful)	3.07
Auto mechanic	11.52
Jet plane captain (average)	33.13
Warren E. Burger	40.70
(chief justice)	
Aerospace factory worker	9.98
Zookeeper (Providence, Rhode Island)	6.47
Steven J. Ross	939.48
(chairman, Warner Communications)	
Public school teacher	8.30
(national average; kindergarten to twelfth grade)	
Sol C. Chaikin	39.65
(president, International Ladies 'Garment Workers' Union)	
Costume design assistant (Broadway)	8.25
Women's garment worker	4.68
Katharine Graham	178.86
(chairman, *Washington Post*)	
Meat packing plant worker	8.83
Major-league baseball umpire (average)	15.38
Sugar Ray Leonard	8,967.26
Tabulator of above (typist)	.04

Their salary levels and talents or contributions are so far out of whack that I cannot bear to tell you what the president of the United States, Pete Rose, Moses Malone, a U.S. senator, Liz Taylor, Frank Sinatra, Mick Jagger, the Pope, or Lech Walesa make for what they do. Compared to David Packard, the cofounder and chairman of Hewlett-Packard, they all are peanut earners. Dave, who must be a fine fellow, had a pretty fair year in the market in

1983. His stockholdings in his company increased $1.2 billion in value. As I said, Lech didn't do that well.

On average, salaries are up approximately 20 percent over 1979 levels. At that pace we'll all be making 20 grand a year by the turn of the century. This ought to work out pretty well because by then a box seat to a major-league baseball game will cost thirty bucks; dress shirts $75; a house in the suburbs, half a million; and a box of laundry detergent, a sawbuck.

Not all remuneration packages fit so neatly into hourly increments. Astronauts and professional jocks, for respectively under- and overpaid reference, are pieceworkers. The former are paid by the death-defying blast-off and powerless reentry, while the latter shovel it in by making assorted spheroids bounce, spin, dribble, soar, curve, putt, and the like to the irrational awe of millions. Perhaps the easiest of all to measure are big-name singers whom you can hire by the tune. According to sources closest to the folk below, any one of them would be pleased to do up a really nice happy birthday phone call for you. Their fees for being so thoughtful are listed to the right. Like everything else in life, they are negotiable.

Streisand	$50,000 (minimum)
Sinatra	$50,000 (more so)
Elton John	$45,000
John Denver	$38,000
Mick Jagger	$35,000
The Eagles	$25,000
Diana Ross	$23,000
Olivia Newton-John	$15,000

All things being equal, take the fifty grand, and have Olivia sing to you three years running. That will leave you with five more to buy yourself a cake or nice new tie. Oh, incidentally, none of the fees include sidemen or anything gaudy in the way of special effects. Lazers, Dolby, and geek turns all are extra.

If you find the concept appealing but do not think you would like to go quite that high for Uncle Harry this year, there are also a number of bargain-basement greetings on the market. Barbara

Eden and Marilyn Michaels (using her Mae West voice) run only $5,000 a call. And the latter will, on the advice of her mother, cut even better deals for unattached young Jewish doctors. Time was that you could get the likes of Barry Manilow, the Captain and Tennille, Willie Nelson, and Johnny Cash for about a grand and a case of Coors, but that time has almost certainly passed. In an ultimate budget crunch, there is always Sonny Bono. Sorry about that. I know it could be a shock to your delicate sensibilities, not to mention eardrums, or those of those you love, but at least the price is right. If you invite Sonny to bring his tenor or bass (or whatever it is) to the party, he will pay you $50. Let him accompany himself on the guitar, and he will up the ante to an even C note. Things do not get expensive at your end unless you bring in a musical director to try to straighten him out. That will cost you $400. An instrumental trio goes for $1,000 but may drown him out and be worth the investment. To have him do it along with them and a singing quartet, you will be in for a $1,300 bill, and if you are not cautious, the adventure could get all the way up to $7,500 with Johnny Mann or Norman Luboff covering for him. Stick with Marilyn's Mae West or even her Edith Bunker. It will be cheaper in the long run, and no one will go home angry or ill.

We digress.

Spending money is easy. Making it (legally) is usually not. As you have already gathered, working for a living is an adequate procedure for those who have to work for a living, but it does not turn out many Harold or Henrietta Heavybucks. If money—real, breathtaking, world-class, go-out-and-buy-yourself-an-island-full-of-nubile-young-sponge-divers-and-their-saronged-cheerleaders money—is what you have in mind, you will need a Plan B. Inheriting someone's hard-earned bundle is a good one. So is winning a lottery or trifecta or Native-American-run bingo game. Best of all is that time-honored favorite: coming up with the proverbial better idea. The world still waits with open pocketbook for those genius types that stride a step or two ahead of the pack's percussion line.

Do not be intimidated by the long shadows of the Pasteurs and

Marconis and Bells and Edisons who have dared daydream before you. Their club, at least its minor-league auxiliary, is not that difficult to join. As evidence pet rocks and mood rings, best-selling inventions do not necessarily include social relevance in their formulas. Even the legitimately functional need not spring from years of plodding experimentation or secret messages from extraterrestrial pyramid builders.

Two of the Patent Office's most celebrated alums, Edwin Land and Dan Gerber, earned their laurels by having the simple good sense to recognize terrific ideas that were not quite yet terrific ideas when they recognized them. Land's son defined a need worth filling by throwing a snit every time he had to wait a week to see the results of smiling for the birdie. Gerber's wife, Dorothy, stumbled them in the general direction of the great little idea hall of fame by being perpetually late for dinner parties and blaming her tardiness on daughter Sally's unmashed vegetables. The results are known today as Polaroid cameras and Gerber baby foods. Both were virtual accidents. Both identified and answered widespread calls for help. Both did so uniquely well. Today both play vital roles in the ongoing chain of matters financial by assuring the uninterrupted flow of undeservedly independent and wealthy future heirs who will never have to punch a clock, thereby leaving coveted positions in the work force open for less fortunate souls that might otherwise fail to find gainful employment and languish on the public doles or become radio personalities, which is darned near as dumb a calling as disc jockey. Messrs. Gerber and Land may not exactly be in Jonas Salk's category, but they will do until some latter-day Ford or Kawasaki assembles a robot that enjoys collecting garbage and diving for sponges.

Such fits of brilliance, like that of the long-ago visionary who got the rest of us moving with the wheel and his or her progeny who brought the masterpiece to its ultimate scientific refinement, the Hula-Hoop, have made their creators justifiably famous and rich. Most of them anyway. Somehow recorded history failed to acknowledge the Old Testament miracle worker who forced the first wonderfully medicinal gulp of chicken soup down her forty-year-old lawyer son's throat. Criminal oversight. No wonder mothers have felt unappreciated ever since.

Mechanical aptitude helps but is not essential. Some of the biggest winners have won on intangibles—that is, good ideas. Ideas like playing catch with used piepans from the Frisbie Baking Company of Bridgeport, Connecticut.* Like Rent-a-Fink, a service which helps gracious hosts and hostesses throw better parties by allowing their guests to feel infinitely superior to the company's staff of professional twerps, who specialize in dull chatter and a general lack of anything approaching intellect. Like balloon bouquets and tap-dancing gorillas and chocolate mousse cake greetings delivered by moonlighting tuxedoed pipefitters or belly-dancing housewives for every occasion. Like all those slightly off-brand religions that promise salvation or five-minute cures for cancer in return for prayers through the radio and Andrew Jacksons through the mail.

Time out! This instant church notion is really worth a second thought. With a little creativity, you and a few close friends could combine your private sects with your favorite hobbies and have one hell (oops, sorry) of a nice plate to pass all the way around. Think about it. Football fanatics could worship St. Dandy at Monday night services without guilt. With a spiritual stamp of approval, philatelists could lick their way to heaven. DQ freaks could carry melting Dilly Bars on their annual pilgrimages to the infinite brazier grill in the sky. And every one of them could get paid for doing so by other nuts that were not swift enough to come up with the idea.

Not, unfortunately, like the bright idea a hapless would-be legend in his own time named Friedrich Brauer had back in 1952. It landed him in the Alsey, Germany, clink for ten weeks. Seems that Fred was caught in the act of buffing gooseberries and trying to sell them as grapes. The brainstorm wasn't his problem. His mistake was trying to market the goodies on his own. Had he sent

---

*Shame the guys who ran the baking company were not bright enough to realize the pans were better than the pies. Frisbie went out of business.

a bunch to K-Tel they probably could have turned his revolutionary berry buffer into an overnight sensation and must stocking stuffer for everyone's mandatory weird uncle who has everything. Barring such success. It was certainly not a dumb enough idea to get him thrown in jail. Not even in the same class, for example, as the few doozies that a self-professed "One-man think tank and Basic Physics Research Laboratory," whose given name was Arthur Paul Pedrick, spent fifteen fruitless years buffing to imperfection. According to an authoritative compendium of such oddities, *The Incomplete Book of Failures,** by Stephen Pile, the prolific Mr. Pedrick earned the dubious distinction of being the all-time least successful inventor by having every one of his 162 patented marvels rejected out of hand by the foolish consuming public. They must not have realized they were missing out on the delights of a golf ball that could be steered in flight, a bicycle with amphibious capacity, eyeglasses that improved vision in bad weather, and automobiles that could be driven from their rear seats. Can you imagine the latter not having caught on with mothers-in-law?

Not all of Pedrick's grand schemes were so frivolous. One might, in fact, have solved the world's hunger problems had it been given half a chance. Again according to researcher Pile, it would have irrigated deserts in every corner of the globe by sending a steady, life-giving flow of snowballs from the polar regions through a network of giant peashooters. Maybe there wasn't anyone in authority devoid enough of hot air to make them work. Art probably should have hired a few ad agency account executives to help get the balls rolling. They had to be able to blow hot and cold on cue to get their jobs.

Hey, they laughed at Leonardo da Vinci, too. All he did between Mona Lisas was sketch and calibrate the helicopter, the submarine, the ball-bearing ring, water skis, scuba diving equipment, bicycles, clockworks, and dozens of other pieces of precision machinery a few hundred years before anyone ever scored three zillion at Pac-Man.

*Yep, the book was a failure.

Jules Verne's funny-looking spaceships were considered an absolute stitch by his contemporaries.

Anyone who was anyone knew the horseless carriage would never replace the real thing.

And indoor plumbing! Who would have dreamed of doing such a thing right in the house?

Great ideas have always been scoffed at and ridiculed. Probably always will be. And they will probably also go right on making millionaires out of the select few (like Thomas Crapper) who could not care less about being scoffed at, rejected by, or dismissed by the masses. Have what it takes? Go for it! Who knows what we all may be doing with giant peashooters a few years from now? Intergalactic plumbing ring your chimes?

Before you go making long-term decisions solely on the basis of bread, however, you had better also consider the fact that while big salaries unquestionably provide amenities denied to most of us, they do not come easily and not without an attendant hazard or two. Third World dictators tend to find themselves couped out of business rather regularly, often unpleasantly. Many great inventions wind up as great explosions. Crooks are often faced with involuntary early retirements. Even wide receivers and hot new starlets face more than an average share of shin splints and hip pointers and the like. All this pales by comparison to what happens to poor correspondents and journalists. They die. Really. Reporters or whatever they are called from one medium to the next have a 30 percent higher mortality rate than that of the population as a whole.

This is not to imply that hazardous duty is restricted to those who enjoy wandering around in the middle of wars and muggings with microphones and steno pads. Everyone faces it. Most do so in the form of stress, which, even though it does not happen to come packaged in fragmenting shell casings, is a real killer. Can you hack one more list? This one is a rip from the always scintillating *Chicago Tribune*. It ranks jobs on the basis of the ulcer juice they brew, number one being the worst.

1. Health technicians
2. Waiters, waitresses
3. Practical nurses
4. Inspectors
5. Musicians
6. Public relations advisers
7. Clinical lab technicians
8. Dishwashers
9. Warehousemen
10. Nurse's aides
11. Laborers
12. Dental assistants
13. Teacher's aides
14. Research workers
15. Computer programmers
16. Photographers
17. Telephone operators
18. Hairdressers
19. Painters, sculptors
20. Health aides (notice a pattern here? Health work is apparently not terribly healthy)
21. Taxicab drivers
22. Chemists
23. Bank tellers
24. Social workers
25. Roofers, slaters
26. Secretaries
27. Nurses, registered
28. Operatives (007 type? They must really be good at it to rank lower than hairdressers)
29. Bakers
30. Structural metal craftsmen
31. Upholsterers
32. Dressmakers
33. Machinists
34. Sales managers
35. Garagemen
36. Clergy
37. Designers

38. Mechanics
39. Clerical workers
40. Office machine operators
41. Guards or watchmen
42. Insurance adjusters
43. Barbers
44. Salesclerks
45. Office managers
46. Editors
47. Teachers
48. Sales representatives
49. Pressmen
50. Painters, construction workers
51. Cooks
52. Engineers
53. Draftsmen
54. Mine operators
55. Tool, diemakers
56. Bookkeepers
57. Food counter people
58. Lumbermen
59. Welders
60. Meat cutters
61. Engineers (the other kind)
62. Brickmasons
63. Insurance agents
64. Furnacemen
65. Electricians
66. Radio or TV repairmen
67. Farmers (owners)
68. Librarians
69. Mail carriers
70. Police
71. Shipping and receiving clerks
72. Real estate agents
73. Carpenters
74. Dietitians
75. Gardeners
76. Pharmacists

77. Accountants
78. Janitors
79. Attendants
80. Truck drivers
81. Maids
82. Firefighters
83. Laundry workers
84. Plumbers
85. Bank financial officers
86. Lawyers
87. Child care workers
88. Dentists
89. Garbage collectors
90. Sawers (no, not seers, sawers)
91. Bus drivers
92. College or university personnel
93. Foresters
94. Cabinetmakers
95. Clerks, counter
96. Electronic technicians
97. Farm laborers
98. Managers, administrators
99. Foremen
100. Housekeepers
101. Vehicle washers
102. Managers, restaurant
103. Cement and concrete workers
104. School administrators
105. Railroad switchmen
106. Doctors
107. Crafts workers
108. Firemen, stationary (whatever that means)
109. Sewer workers
110. Telephone linemen
111. Fork-lift operators
112. Heavy-equipment operators
113. Packers and wrappers
114. Officials and administrators, government
115. Buyers

116. Electrical power linemen
117. Personnel-labor relations
118. Health administrators
119. Freight handlers
120. Decorators
121. Engineering science technicians
122. Surveyors
123. Checkers and examiners (quality control)
124. Professional technicians
125. Stock handlers
126. Ticket agents
127. Chemical technicians
128. Tailors
129. Hucksters (sales people)
130. Dyers

No, I really do not know why the list does not include astronauts, middle linebackers, chorus girls, chorus boys, radio announcers, or bomb defusers. Part of the reason may be the simple fact that it is a 1977 list. In 1977, as you may recall, trend setters were still wearing polyester leisure suits and hose without built-in panties. Times have changed, and opportunities have changed with them. There are plenty of perfectly gut-wrenching assignments today which did not even exist way back in the once upon a time days before Luke Skywalker. Among them:

Elvis clones: up 5,000 percent since the original went to that great rhinestone caddyshack in the sky.

E.T. and Gremlin everything makers.

Park district soccer coaches: Very high tension because of the difficulty men who grew up admiring Willie Mays have in trying to memorize their kids' new heroes' names. Much less their positions.

Personal computer salespeople: Very lucrative but how often can you explain disk drive without having your memory hashed and pitching your chips? Great second career for out-of-work used car peddlers, though.

Unisex boutique operator: Suddenly everyone is tired of looking unisexy.

Watergate trivia expert: The market has gone soft, and pressure is intense to be the first on the rubber chicken circuit positively to identify "Deep Throat." Big bucks if you can cut it.

Microwave TV chef: Have any idea how nerve-racking it must be to have to plan a half hour's worth of recipes every day when the damn thing bakes potatoes in four minutes?

Video game master: Having to master a brand-new best game ever invented every other day is no weekend in Plains.

Gloria Vanderbilt or Brooke Shields.

A reporter for the *National Enquirer*: The assignments are not all that harrowing, but the excruciating threat of accidentally telling the truth must always hang there like a cloud.

PATCO shop steward.

Dedicated craftsperson: Being an endangered species can get to you after a while.

Female chief exec: Extremely tense unless you also happen to be homely enough to look as though you had made it on brains or pull.

Non-Japanese mogul: Regardless of sex, see "Dedicated craftsperson" for details.

Someone on a high-sodium diet: The stigma is absolutely unbearable.

Owner of a mechanical bull factory.

Someone who does not listen when E. F. Hutton speaks.

One who once had the other kind of herpes and thought nothing of saying so.

A librarian: Lonesomeness can be hell.

The maker of medium-size radios.

Someone who got out of the jogging shoe business in 1977.

It is not accidental that several of those entries are more avocational than occupational. Getting a job, any job, may be tough until the nation's economic turnaround is complete or McDonald's sells its billionth IntergalacticMac on Mars—whichever comes first—so inclusion of a few free-time activities seemed in order. Besides, even if you are fortunate enough to find work, you will need a little something on the side to help unwind after a hard day at the mines. Getting a feel for the available diversions may help you settle on the life role from which you will want to be diverted. You would not, after all, want to do anything too enjoyable for a living because you would then not be able to look desperately forward to vacations and weekends. Not looking desperately forward to vacations and weekends is un-American.

In any event, barring the happy accident of sole kinship to someone very old and very wealthy, in which case all this is academic, you have a heavy decision ahead. At the risk of redundancy, it will count. Mix and match the upsides and downs carefully. Henceforth you will be indelibly imprinted as a pipe fitter or neurosurgeon or baton twirler or nuclear physicist or palm-frond weaver or whatever indelible imprint you pick. Henceforth is a long time. Pick well.

5

Get Smarts

Think picking the perfect job was tough? Wait until you have to go out and actually try to get it! *Tough* is not the word for this phase of enforced maturation. *Impossible* is not the word either, but what with jammed waiting rooms, autobiography-length application forms in triplicate, and sweaty-palmed interviews, this phase of the enforced maturation ritual is enough to make what you have already been through seem like a couple of weeks on Maui.

The basic villains at work here are selfishness and unrealistic goals. Everyone else's. Although logic and anthropology agree that available work and available workers ought to balance out in a civilized society, not enough of your competitors in the job market are usually willing to cooperate with the plan. Hardly any of them, for example, will have had the simple good sense to grow up dreaming of becoming any of the things that you have given reasonable review and even more reasonable rejection. This short-sightedness crowds the field for us legitimate beach bum and jet set candidates. And because the demand for qualified newcomers in such specialties has waned so dramatically since Frankie's, Annette's, and Jackie O's heydays, it means that slicing your rightful piece of the pie is going to take luck, energy, and preparation. Most of all, preparation. Without it, you may show up at the right place at the right time with the wrong stuff. There is nothing in life more frustrating and counterproductive. Just ask William F. Buckley, Jr. The poor man's abilities have always been so out of touch with demand that he hasn't been able to avoid an honest day's work in his entire life. The resultant trauma has caused him to suffer the rare double affliction of Tonguis Dartis-outis and Pompous Overactis first identified and dwelled upon in the learned tome *To Be or Not to Be, Either Way Sounds Good to Me*, by the equally self-professed authority on almost everything, Gore Vidal.

Dangerous waters. To avoid them, get the tools you will need to succeed in the real world. Once you have Chinese menued your way through your career options and their best bet payoffs, build yourself a package of marketable credentials. Charm, wit, ambition, and a flair for office politics all are worth developing, but the one indispensable will be a good, well-rounded education.

Someone once said a good, well-rounded education "is one which prepares its recipient to respond intelligently when asked in later life to define a good, well-rounded education."

Someone else said, "It's knowin' what it takes to get the job done, then knowin' how to get someone else to do it."

Both notions make sense, but they lack the ring of authentic officialese, without which most bureaucrats and other pillars of the community are uncomfortable. For their edification, the diction- ary says, "ed'u-ca'tion (-ka'shun), n., is the act or process of edu- cating; discipline of mind or character through study, instruction or observation; also, a stage of such a process or the training in it; as, to receive a college education."

Ah, yes, college—that four-, five-, or six-year sabbatical from reality during which the cream of American youth's total assign- ment is to lie around alternately thinking great thoughts and party- ing, not necessarily in that order. A mental marathon designed to provide basic proficiency in a myriad of such handy everyday skills as metaphysics, Elizabethan drama, and the use of schmancy words like *myriad* while one simultaneously unlocks the elitist mysteries of ivy-clung tradition, blue books, pompons, quads (a.k.a. commons and greens on hard-core ivy campuses), food fights, orientation lectures, kegs, pantie raids, togas, all-nighters, secret handshakes, the Greek alphabet, orals, cuts, more kegs, football weekends, endless registration lines, synopses, curves, all-but-invisible profs and omnipresent proctors, midterms, spring breaks, Jockey shorts raids, cramming, and graduation ceremonies with names no one can pronounce, much less survive in a state of consciousness. College. The stuff of dreams and rah-rah legend.

Now, with all that and Mr. Webster's endorsement as one of the better ways to go about disciplining mind and character going for the collegiate experience, the decision facing anyone with an ounce of scholarly affectation or rich parents is not whether to matriculate but where. This decision, like most others worth making, depends heavily upon desired results. It's like, y'know, whaddaya wanna be when you grow up?

No easy call. Colleges and their curricula are many and varied. They come in all shapes, sizes, and geographies. They each have strengths. They each have soft spots. A nice one named Harvard that a myriad (see how much smarter you are already?) of over-achievers seem to admire, for example, does pretty well with future presidents but has not turned out a dominant NBA center in years. Southern Cal and Alabama, on the other hand, are somewhat better known for their modern tailbacks than for their ancient historians. Georgetown clones endless international diplomats and CIA agents but fails miserably when the call goes out for scuba divers and rodeo clowns, both of whom you will find aplenty at Miami and Oregon State respectively, where there are usually zero prospective UN types running around. Engineers abound at MIT and Purdue. Neither, however, has ever to my direct knowledge got the hang of teaching podiatry. Northwestern and UCLA make moviemakers by the Oscar-winning dirty dozen, but their quotas of delicatessen slicers go unfilled year after year. And so it goes.

The only exceptions to the rules are those extremely rare institutions of higher learning that have somehow resisted the urge to academic myopia and the residual benefits of which are so universal as to play well in virtually any future setting. *Extremely rare* is an understatement. There are precisely three from which to choose: McDonald's, Notre Dame, and the Armand Hammer United World College of the American West.

Golden Arches Tech, as it is lovingly remembered by its budding Managers on Duty and Filet-o-Fishists cum laude, teaches state-of-the-art burger scorching and ketchup dolloping. One who has mastered these skills will never be at a loss for friends or fortune.

Regardless of career calling, ND grads will always have the inner peace and tranquillity that comes from being able to wander around for the rest of their lives getting all teary-eyed every time they pass a yellow roof or football and humming what they know to be "the" one true fight song deserving of the name. Interestingly they may be right. "Cheer, cheer . . ." is the fourth most identifiable tune of any kind in this country. Know the other three? Must not have been to college yet.

Products of good old Armand Hammer UWC etc., in Montezuma, New Mexico, with sister institutions in Wales, British Columbia, Singapore, Swaziland, and Trieste, Italy, will ever be a similarly well-adjusted lot. This, according to its recruitment brochure, is because they will have learned, under the guidance and presidency of HRH the Prince of Wales, things "likely to foster better understanding of the steps necessary to mitigate rivalries and conflicts that divide races and nations everywhere." They will also have picked up a minor in mountain search and rescue. Hard to go wrong with that kind of diversified academic background. As if it were not enough, there is the bonus of not having to sit around learning how to make small talk. This is because the entire student body is only 200 strong, and it is drawn from fifty different countries. You would be surprised at how seldom you fall into idle chitchatting when no one understands anyone else's chit or chat.

Sadly, such catholic and practical learning experiences become progressively more difficult to obtain as one bastion of lofty generality after another bites the dust. Not long ago Parsons College in Fairfield, Iowa, stopped pumping out the classics and transcendentally meditated itself into Maharishi International U.—the one and probably only seat of higher learning where students are en-

couraged to come to class in sheets and major, literally, in levita-
tion. Most recently the one and definitely only College of
Lawsonomy, long revered in academic circles for having consistently created the world's finest Lawsonomists, closed its hal-
lowed halls forever. While no official reason for the decision was
given, it is widely believed to have been a result of consensus
within those same academic circles that the job market and polo
fields were already glutted with more than enough well-trained
pupils of Lawsonomy.*

An irrevocable loss to be sure but not irreplaceable. There are
still plenty of almost equally esoteric spots at which to learn darned
near anything else that you care to learn. Tens of thousands of
them if you count the Nashville College of Electronic Auto and
Truck Repair or the Reverend Mr. Falwell's favorite, Liberty Bap-
tist, or the individual parts of the hundreds of places called univer-
sities which are actually colleges of colleges clustered around
common landmark statues or football stadia or domes or steeples.
Mostly domes or steeples. The world of higher learning is very big
on domes and steeples, so be sure to have one or both handy if you
ever decide to emulate old Al and start a college or university of
your very own in later life. Also, be absolutely certain to follow
Clark Kerr's three mandatory rules for a successful college:
". . . have plenty of football for the alumni, sex for the students,
and parking for the faculty." In the meantime, pay more attention
to those less evident measurement criteria which might help you
pick one of the schools someone else has already founded. Things
like the number of Nobel laureates on the faculty or fraternities
and sororities on campus. Even things like the schools themselves.
Some are quite famous; others, rather closely guarded family secrets. Some are as large and bustling as Lincoln, Nebraska; others,
as pristine and conducive to intellectual growth as latter-day Wal-
den ponds. A select few demand adherence to strict standards of
student behavior. A majority could not care less if you partied

---

*The in-depth study of everything founder Alfred Lawson ever thought about anything
he ever thought about, which included almost everything.

yourself purple every night of the week. Most do, however, have one or two bits of common ground. They all offer B.A.'s and B.S.'s and M.'s and Ph.D.'s of various orders. A few of the real biggies add L.L.D.'s, B.C.E.'s, M.C.E.'s, and the like. One, Detroit, even has a few rare LTDs and GTOs available. They all also cost an arm and a leg and several of your patron's other more or less vital parts. As a result, the family vaults will certainly play as much of a role in your ultimate choice of colors as will your personal priorities and mental acumen. Think positively. For the moment, presume the finances to be in order and go ahead with the intricate selection process. Far better to do so sooner than later. You may eventually have to pay for such things as higher education yourself.

Planning to be a mover, shaker, and country club champ? One or more sheets of prestigious sheepskin will be an absolute prerequisite. According to Rosenblatt's law (like Kerr's aforementioned rules), one of many such insightful dicta to be found in Paul Dickson's *The Official Explanations*, upper crustiness is a relatively easy collegiate attribute to track. It states, ". . . the further east one's university, the more honored he is the further west he travels." If such is your want, by all means consider Harvey Mudd or one of the other squash powers to the right of Appalachia the elite alumni rosters of which are exceeded only by their even eliter endowment troves. If the Fortune 500 dabbled in academe, its top ten would probably read like the Ivy League's final season standings. Not so coincidentally, most of its headliners would also find comfortably musty spots in the history books. Some are older than most states. Harvard, for an admittedly redundant example, was founded all the way back in 1636. It was followed by William and Mary (1693), Yale (1701), Penn (1740), and Moravian (1742). Oddly, the still-renowned Transylvania U. didn't open its drawbridges until 1780. No, its team mascot does not wear a cape or have fangs. That's rumored to be one of its deans. Nothing particularly unique in that. Deans everywhere have capes and fangs.

If the gusher out on the back forty has already assured your social status in perpetuity and you are merely seeking a gaudy tuition level appropriate to your means, many of the same essentially eastern institutions qualify. Such things are seldom discussed in polite company, but best guessers guess that at $17,000 and change a year, MIT (Massachusetts Institute of Technology to those who do not run with the academic in crowd) is probably the single most expensive domestic alma mater that Daddy's bucks and your brains can buy. In alphabetical order, others with reasonable shots at breaking the bank include:

Amherst
Bryn Mawr
California Institute of Technology
Carnegie-Mellon
Chicago
Columbia
Dartmouth
Duke
Georgetown
Harvard/Radcliffe
Johns Hopkins
Mount Holyoke
Northwestern
Pennsylvania
Princeton
Simons Rock of Bard
Smith
Southern California
Stanford
Wellesley
Williams
Yale

All fall somewhere in the $15,000 per annum range. Naturally, these lowball estimates do not include such plebeian incidentals as books, clothing, and travel. But then, when a slice of sheephide from Simons Rock of Bard is at stake, who can be bothered worrying about trivialities?

Proper decorum and a foundation in the social graces are said to play important roles in some occupations. Though it is difficult to imagine what such occupations might be, if you have chosen one, pack your waistcoat and Emily Post and head directly, though genteelly to be sure, for Agnes Scott, Hollins, Ohio Wesleyan, Virginia, Washington and Lee, or William and Mary. They excel at inculcating trappings of the effete.

At the distinctly opposite end of the spectrum are those less formal Acadias which leave one better prepared for life's weekends than its stockholder meetings. To put it another way, if parties are your thing, look no further than:

Alabama
Arizona
Boston
Bucknell
Clemson
Colorado
Delaware
Dickinson
Emory
Florida
Georgia
Indiana
Ithaca
Miami
New Mexico
Ohio
Southern Illinois
Southern Methodist
Syracuse
Texas
Texas Christian
Tulane
Vanderbilt
Vermont
Virginia
Washington and Lee
William and Mary
Wisconsin

Virginia, Washington and Lee, and William and Mary must obviously be something special. The fact that they somehow managed to make both the ultrarefined and ultra-Animal House listings means one of two things. They either offer the world's roundest well-rounded educations or throw some very dull bashes.

Looking for a sexually segregated environment? How come? None of my business. You want to be a monk, be a monk. Get thee to a nunnery. No, on second thought, that might not work out so well. Best check out Wabash, Goucher, or Mount Holyoke instead. Until recently William and Mary would have made this list as well. That place is starting to sound downright weird. Next thing you know someone will probably build a wall around its adjacent town and make you buy tickets to take a walk down cobblestoned streets while the locals pretend to be their great-great-great-great-or-so-grandparents.

This entire prematriculation exercise is much easier for those who have had the good fortune to pick their careers while still at the secondary level. They have it knocked because they can pick a college on the basis of very specific strengths. Plantation heirs and others dedicated to the proposition that tobacco is a terribly misunderstood wonder drug, for instance, will be most comfortable at Kent State, Carleton, or Marlboro. Future dentists cannot do much better than Colgate. Cheese freaks should definitely check out Colby. For horticulturists, there are Sweet Briar and Evergreen State. Hunter is probably a good bet for people who enjoy blowing away unsuspecting beasts. And Scripps sounds perfect for writers who cannot spell, which about takes in the field. Even Yeshiva and Quinnipiac have their respective niches. Both are great training grounds for avid Scrabble players.

By now you have no doubt been able to narrow your options. Outstanding. Now for your next trick, get admitted to the school you have picked. Again, no easy matter. There are SATs and ACTs and forms and applications and admissions officer interviews and enough Byzantine companion entrance requirements ahead to support a booming cottage industry. One of its more usable by-products is a thoroughly readable—more unusual than it sounds— entrance primer called *The Insider's Guide to the Colleges*. Published annually by living, breathing, not to mention reasonably articulate and opportunistic Yale undergrads, it goes far beyond the normal, mundane information concerning successful applicants' test medians and faculty-student ratios and admission criteria. It gets into the really important material like various schools' cafeteria and laundry services, dorm visitation privileges, and the estimated number of on-campus rock concerts per semester. An indicative sampling of its salient observations includes:

. . . the college experience has only a coincidental relation to the official process of education.

Many students, even at the "best" colleges, regard classes and books as annoying details.

Arizona State, Arkansas, Drake, Michigan State, and Ohio State are among the easiest schools to stay in once in.

There are only two types of high school guidance counselors . . . neither will be of much use to you.

College students always tell their parents that they study until two in the morning. They occasionally omit the fact that they don't usually start studying until after midnight and seldom wake up before noon.

In analyzing a college or university, visit and look around to size up the students with whom you may be living. Notice if their eyes are glazed and skin clammy. Do they babble unintelligibly while puffing on the wrong end of filter cigarettes? Do words like "intense" dominate their vocabularies? Do they struggle around under the weight of their calculators and slide rules?

It may sound odd, but you can also tell quite a lot about schools from their athletic cheers. Places where student sections excitedly chant, "Suppress them, suppress them, make them relinquish the orb," for instance, are not likely to be as entertaining as those where "Two bits, four bits" fills the air on Saturday afternoons.

Do not lay it on too thick when applying. Admissions officers have very sensitive bullshit detectors. Besides, by the time they get to your application form, they will be near nausea at the sight of another class president, student council officer, debate team captain, basketball captain, math team captain, yearbook editor, honor board member, and all of that.

The most important thing about the formal interview is to give the other guy a good time.

One crucial point: Keep your parents at least a thousand feet and preferably a thousand miles away from the interview session.

If the interview makes you nervous, imagine him sitting in his underwear and, whatever else happens, do not walk off with his pen. [The underwear gamut does not work as well for male applicants if the interviewer is female.]

Under penalty of death, do not be cool. [This does not mean that you should overtly beg for admission. Just avoid leaving the impression that you could not give a damn about the stupid joint. This is often considered a negative in interview situations.]

SAT's and ACT's are real pains.

The veracity of this last particular insight is underscored by the following typical questions which were lifted directly from one or the other.

Select the lettered pair that best expresses a relationship similar to that expressed in the original pair.
MALLEABLE:FASHIONED
(A) amenable:swayed
(B) baleful:praised
(C) amicable:engendered
(D) intangible:measured
(E) mandatory:punished

Direct transmission electron microscopy would probably be LEAST useful in the study of which of the following:
(A) Pathological microorganisms
(B) A biological section one cell thick
(C) A semi-transparent flake of mica
(D) Finely ground grains of quartz sand
(E) A sheet of limestone with small imbedded fossils

Integers p and q are said to be "semirelated" if p is an even number and q is twice p. For which of the following pairs of numbers (p,q) are p and q NOT "semirelated"?

(A) (2,4)
(B) (3,6)
(C) (4,8)
(D) (10,20)
(E) (22,44)

Nuff said?

In the final analysis, interviewers like to give the impression that all applicants are judged more on the basis of their whole multidimensional picture as delineated by paper qualifications than on the basis of their clout. This is not necessarily a correct impression.

Society is about to give you four years to play games, be irresponsible and think about thing before you start playing for keeps. You can march, protest, sing, dance, smoke, drink, fool around, waste time, holler, shout, and be as foolhardy as you want, and nobody is going to do anything about it.

That about sums it up. If this primer-level introduction to academe didn't do it for you, nothing will. This may be okay. As noted earlier, college is one of the better ways to go about getting smart. But it is not the only way and not necessarily even the correct way for everyone. In fact, a majority of downright successful folks never made it to, much less through, Vassar or Hofstra or even Florida A&M. They earned their credits and learned their stuff on the toughest, biggest, baddest track of all: the School of Hard Knocks. Some attended good old SHK's innumerable street-corner extensions. Others opted for factory, farm, or armed forces courses. A very progressive and unusual few even took advantage of unlikely tutelage in the privacy of their very own homes. Believe it or not, relatives, even parents, occasionally say something almost bright.

These incidentally, perhaps even accidentally educated winners include Andrew Carnegie, Charlie Chaplin, Buffalo Bill Cody, Noel Coward, Charles Dickens, Isadora Duncan, Thomas

Edison, Samuel Gompers, John Philip Sousa, and Mark Twain, among others, who never made it past grade school; Harry Belafonte, Cher, Mary Baker Eddy, Henry Ford, George Gershwin, Adolf Hitler, Dean Martin, all of the Beatles and Rolling Stones, Bill Mauldin, Rod McKuen, Steve McQueen, Al Pacino, Will Rogers, William Saroyan, Frank Sinatra, Robert Wagner, and the flying brothers Wrights, none of whom ever made it through high school; and Joseph Chamberlain, Grover Cleveland, Joseph Conrad, Aaron Copland, Amelia Earhart, Kahlil Gibran, Ernest Hemingway, Rudyard Kipling, Abraham Lincoln, H. L. Mencken, John D. Rockefeller, Eleanor Roosevelt, George Bernard Shaw, Dylan Thomas, Josip Tito, Harry Truman, George Washington, and Virginia Woolf, who made it in but not out of one college or another before becoming famous, infamous, or both.

Their lead is clear. The idea is to make the grade, with or without the "grades." Formal education and intellectualism are fine. Intelligence is a whole lot better. Do not confuse the two. Read books if that is what you like to do. Talk to people whether that is what you like to do or not. More important, listen. Smell flowers, and watch ants build itty-bitty condos and prepare to take over the world. Pound a nail into something hard. Spend one evening a year with the TV turned off. By all means, spend an absolute minimum of one summer vacation doing something physically demanding, ideally something that makes you sweat or, as they say around the old school, perspire. Whatever you do, get what you need and use what you have. The best is coming on so fast it may slip right on by if you are anything less than ready, willing, and able to grab on for the ride.

6

After Hours

Man does not make it by bread or brains alone. Nor does woman. Both demand something more out of life than slabs of imitation sheepskin or punch clock elbow, something for the soul, something private, fulfilling, and, best case, darned near pointless. Since the world is absolutely loaded with fulfilling, darned near pointless things to do in one's best case private moments after the daily grind, this is good.

Variously, lovingly known as hobbies, pastimes, diversions, kicks, and off-the-job training, these emotionally essential slices of the good life lump rather nicely under the catchall heading of "recreation"—literally "the act of creating anew, refreshing strength and spirit after toil." That's the plan all right, and its undeniable urgency makes these get-away-from-it-alls matter much more than they probably should. This, too, is good because vestiges of the sixties' flower power and the seventies' social relevance syndromes still get in the way of more than enough perfectly pointless activities for generations of dedicated workaholics. Left unchecked, they can wind your string so tight you forget how to smile. Don't let them. Lay back for your rights. Tuck those progressively more noticeable jowls as far in as nature allows and bellow the remedial rallying cry of the eighties, "Make fun, not ulcers!," as you map your escape route. And don't just say it.

Mean it! You deserve a day in the park, and if you pass the chance while you have it, you will have no one to blame except yourself. You haven't got enough grief already without adding a guilt trip to the bundle? Work at defining your idea of play. Then go for it no matter what it is. Happily the options are limitless.

Have an undiscovered world-class jock or jockette buried somewhere inside those pillows and pouches? Awesome! By all means let him or her out. According to the Perrier Study of Fitness in America (no, I'm not really sure why its sponsors wanted to study fitness in America when they already had a lock on our infinitely more lucrative gullibility quotient, but to show your gratitude for the honor and glory of it all [not to mention the Statue of Liberty and Brigitte Bardot], the next time you feel like paying two bucks for a glass of water be sure to say, "Make mine Perrier"), a veritable Olympiad awaits the opportunity to test your personal best. On the basis of participation, the survey ranks our top forms of voluntary exercise as walking (22 percent), swimming (17 percent), calisthenics (14 percent), bicycling (13 percent), running or jogging (11 percent), tennis (9 percent), basketball (7 percent), hiking (7 percent), softball (7 percent), and baseball (6 percent). Those parenthetical percentages are drawn from The Average American (a jam-packed statman's dream of a paperback which proves once and for all that we have no secrets) and supposedly represent the number of us who do each when we get the chance. If one of them sounds like the sort of thing you might enjoy having pop your pecs into some semblance of shape, be sure to consider its probable advantages and drawbacks closely before you go making a decision likely to affect your big, fine bod for life.

1. Walking: Certainly a harmless enough entry-level activity ("exercise" seems a bit too ambitious a description for the act of putting one foot in front of the other without necessarily moving your lips). Nothing to it, in fact, unless you count such hazards as errant sprinklers and doggy doo. Not much of an adventure either, unless it is done a few feet behind someone healthier-looking than you or while you are attached to stress tester machinery with twenty minutes yet to

go on a twenty-five-minute exam. Still, more than 96 million people claim to do it for some loftier reason than getting to and from the john, so who am I to say it should not count? Maybe they are actually referring to "purposeful walking." I tried to confirm this possibility with my doctor, but he does not have a phone on his golf cart.

Rating: Good for the cardiovascular system. Not necessarily terrific for the feet. On the whole, just so-sole.

2. Swimming (75 million reported regular, albeit damp, users): More like it! The all-time favorite of octogenarian world leaders and insufferably freckled Norman Rockwell juveniles alike, this most primal of contemporary sports is best described as a tribute to Kermit the Frog. Why 70 or 80 million people a year choose to play soggy tribute to a frog, a pretend frog at that, is a mystery, but then, since its proper execution requires one's total immersion and little or no attire, it is replete with mysterious psychological and anthropological implications. Once you get a few of your more important parts used to the cold water, it can be a pretty nice time as well.

Rating: A definite winner. The skinny-dipping kind even gets four stars On Golden Pond.

3. Calisthenics: Talk about knowing how to have a good time! What could be more fun than bending, stretching, and straining yourself into catatonic lather three or four times a week? Fifty-some millions of our otherwise normal-looking compatriots apparently can't think of a thing. Each to his own. Eight-count Burpies and Saturday Night Specials are by far their favorites. That figures. Both are appropriately named. Both are vomit-inducing. Both are completely nuts. I, for one, cannot figure out how the category got so highly ranked. Perhaps the fieldworkers were on Perrier at the time, and too much of the fizz made it to their heads. Either that or Barbarella is a far more convincing aerobics Pied Piper than political activist. No doubt about her credentials.

Rating: Why would you want to do something like that to a nice person like you? What if you can't get untangled someday or get busted for heavy breathing on the way home? What would your relatives think?

4. Bicycling: Much more like it! Everyone ought to have wheels. Indispensable for those who have gas guzzlers or paper routes and easily the most pleasant, relaxing, healthful to mind and body, and aesthetically rewarding experience imaginable. Besides, my daughter could use a new one, and who knows, maybe one of the Schwinn boys got this dubious masterpiece as an April Fools' Day present. Rating: Excellent. Simply excellent. It even makes you feel smarter. Once you learn how to do it, you will never forget. Bet you can't say that about algebra or isometrics.

5. Running or jogging (45 million deranged blister bearers at last bouncing head count): Based on psycho-cuckoo theories first popularized by that immortal physical fitness buff the Marquis de Sade, both forms of self-inflicted punishment are among the most advanced stages of the deviate behavior which can result from experimentation with calisthenics in early life. Their supposed goal is the attainment of a state of quasi-spiritual nirvana via a senses-numbing series of solo marathons. Although no longer quite as widely abused as they were before most fad-conscious radio performers and other misguided people discovered that knees tend to be less resilient than automotive shock absorbers, approximately 25 million joggers and/or runners (as its militants shamelessly call themselves) still swear by jogging and/or running respectively. For the sake of perspective, it should be noted that a majority of really hard-core lingering enthusiasts are not participants per se. They are bone specialists, charity race organizers, and the makers of heliotrope sweat suits with pink piping or sponge rubber stereo earmuffs.

Rating: If you are not a big fan of shin splints, orthoscopic surgery, or hypothermia, or worse, you can do better. Try biking. It is more fun, and besides, I know this adorable kid who could really use a new one.

6. Tennis: Unless there are now approximately 35 million members of the officially recognized elite, tennis is no longer the exclusive game of the elite. What it is is an extremely efficient way to telescope all the exhaustion inherent to any more civilized sport into a nice compact period of blazing insanity. Relatively inexpensive, once your $20,000 court and five grand lighting system have been installed. Also simple to play as long as you are fourteen years old, have arms that bend backward in two or three places, enjoy cussing

at grown men and women who never grew out of high chairs, and can keep score in Byzantine code. Know what I mean, love? Attributed to an unknown patron, the calling (somehow sport seems a bit plebeian here) hath ten commandments.

1. Thou shalt have no sport other than tennis.
II. Thou shalt remember thy appointed court time.
III. Thou shalt honor thy backhand as instructed by thy pro.
IV. Thou shalt not bear false witness to end lines.
V. Thou shalt not taketh the name of the Lord in vain when thy shot hitteth the tape and faileth to roll over.
VI. Thou shalt not destroyeth thy racket after having lobbed directly to thy opponent at the net.
VII. Thou shalt not commit double fault at set point.
8. (Sorry, I couldn't keep the column straight with a Roman numeral VIII.) Thou shalt not steal thy partner's overhead smash.
IX. Thou shalt not covet thy neighbor's partner.
X. Thou shalt not useth four-letter expletives when thou hast caused an early volley to be ensnared by the net.

Rating: Aces all the way. Especially if you swing graphite. Incidentally, other racket sports are also growing in popularity. One outstanding example is platform tennis, which can only be played out of doors in New York City in the middle of January. At the risk of overstating the obvious, it is most popular with those odd enough to play games out of doors in New York City in the middle of January. New York elitists who prefer the comforts of salt water against blazing sunburn tend to forgo the courts altogether and blow 4 or 5 million a summer trying to make American sailboats faster than Australian sailboats.

7. Basketball (estimated number of cagers—no, I don't know why basketball players are called cagers—however many kids live near playgrounds): Well, all right, now we're getting somewhere! Here's a game that anyone can master in a flash. Although being six feet eight inches and black doesn't hurt, no less an authority than the coach, Ray Meyer of DePaul, once told me that even slow-footed white kids (something of a redundancy there) can sometimes almost get the hang of it. If the coach says so, take it to the bank. Aquire and Cummings and Mikan and Corzine certainly have.

Rating: Definitely above the rim. For best results, be sure to think up a terrific new name and work on your outer space/in your face/phi slamma jamma dunk.

8. Hiking (20 plus millions, not counting parking lot attendants or ticket scalpers): Basically walking with poison ivy and moose droppings in place of the urban variety of obstacles. For the purpose of this learned treatise, think of hiking as a generic representative of a myraid of other favorites of those rugged individualists who enjoy communing with nature at odd hours and, usually, killing things. These kindred flannel shirt and hobnail boot expressions of outdoorsy creative release include hunting, fishing, backpacking, berry picking, mountain climbing, white-water rafting, wilderness survival training, snipe catching, guerrilla skulking, and the great outdoors' answer to the family hour: camping. Ah, yes, camping. Embers crackling under a moonlit sky, mosquitoes buzz-bombing in every direction, creepy noises in the jungle night—nothing blows away the oppressive congestion of city life like the oppressive congestion of the campground and its chemical latrines; pay showers with cold and cold dribbling water just a half mile past the cesspool or all-night provisions trailer with Rodeo Drive prices; horseflies the size of horseflies; and, once-in-a-lifetime sites complete with converted oil can garbage can and a view of a tree and intermittently functioning hookups. All for only ten or fifteen scrones a night plus the downstroke for your luxury Winnebago, which almost never fits into the first three absolutely once-in-a-lifetime sites you pick, thereby effectively neutralizing the advantage you gained by abandoning the preceding day's once-in-a-lifetime site at three in the morning. Any wonder why hiking is so popular?

Rating: Recommended for people with beards and Smokey the Bear hats who appreciate the once-in-a-lifetime thrill of bumping into rockslides and rattlesnakes. All others, try biking. It gets you sunburned and dirty and everything just like this stuff but leaves out the horseflies.

9. Softball (12 million hardy souls with protruding pots and other questionably athletic qualifications): Perhaps the quintessential American game (at worst a tie with pitching pennies), it combines fellowship, dust, gallons of beer, colorfully contoured uniforms, and an almost total lack of demand for athletic prowess of any kind into a

high-scoring, low-vocabulary experience in excellence for closet Dale Murphys of every age everywhere. Well, almost everywhere. The game's epicenter is Chicago, Illinois, where lifelong purists disdain the pansy version, which utilizes wimpy little balls, gloves, and aluminum bats in place of the genuine articles. Softball Chicago style settles for nothing less than a honeydew melon-size sack of mush that splats on contact with good old hunks of hickory and wobbles into bare hands or, as often as not, watermelon-size bellies. So advanced is the level of competition that such mound legends as Harold "the Underdog" Washington, Mike "the Spike" Royko, Jumbo Larson, and the mightiest of them all, Ed ("Chicago") Schwartz, actually put up with regular jobs the rest of the year just to keep properly out of shape for the season.

Rating: Sublime. As pointless an activity as you will find anywhere. There ought to be a hall of fame, but a corner bar will do and usually does.

10. Baseball (8 or 9 million active players, 11 of whom are grown-ups): Basically softball for millionaires, kids, and sissies, baseball is the simplest of the lot. Its action, what there is of it, revolves around the stylized machinations of two key players. One, the pitcher, stands on top of a piece of rubber sixty feet six inches away from another, the batter, and repeatedly flings a leather rock in his general direction at the approximate speed of sound. The latter tries to propel it back at the former with the help of a spit-shined club (unless the latter happens to be named George Brett, in which case the club will probably be more pined than shined). Two other guys—one a player, one not—squat behind the batter, wearing mattresses and birdcages. The player spends most of his time wiggling his fingers between his legs while the nonplayer keeps yelling about balls and strikes. (A kind of gross game when you think about it.) All the other players, and there are a flat gang of them on both teams, alternately stand around behind the pitcher, scratching and chanting, "Ay, battah . . . ay, battah," or sitting in a little hole on the side of the field, spitting and imploring each other either to "get it started" or to "keep it going." The object of the players standing around scratching is to get the other players out so they can go in and spit, at which point those who had been sitting around spitting have to go out and start scratching. This goes on until the nonplayer behind the batter has had enough of it and tells everyone to go home. Really

exciting. It does have one big problem, though. Like cow chip chucking, curling, and many other team sports, it is sometimes difficult to get up a game. This is because there are not available all that many people over nine years of age who enjoy scratching and spitting and having leather rocks thrown at them. Bob Newhart was right.

Rating: Without a network contract, forget it.

Notice anything odd about the list? I sure did. So much so that I am seriously considering demanding a recount. How could bowling, car racing, pinochle, golf, wind surfing, doing Lite beer commercials, and sex not have made the top ten? C'mon, give me a break! Perhaps the problem is one of semantics. The stats were identified as exercise-related. A recreation peg would no doubt have jumbled the entries dramatically. Never one to take a stand when a bet is there to be hedged, I shall work on the assumption that I missed a couple of pages and ad-lib it for them.

BOWLING: Perfect off-season maintenance for inestimable millions of softballers and their groupies. (Of course, softballers have groupies. What kind of big-time macho sport would it be without someone to show off for?) Not recommended for those who can see their feet without the help of a mirror. The idea is to act cool under the intense scrutiny of your peers after having bounced a rubber cannonball at ten wooden milk bottles with Daffy Duck collars painted around their necks. If you knock down all the bottles in one or two bounces or, likely story, perfect rolls, you get to smile humbly on your way back to the bench and buy beer for everyone you have ever met. It's a pretty big honor. You also get to put an X on a piece of paper. Each X is worth 10 points plus whatever number of bottles you obliterate in ensuing attempts up to a total of three Xs in a row. At that point some kind of new math takes effect, and twelve Xs in a row wind up being worth a total of 300. Very few keglers (authentic jargon once again) ever get twelve in a row and are usually so excited when they do that no one seems to mind the oddball addition. Most people who play the game get some /'s and regular numbers and a few zeros mixed in with their occasional Xs. As a bonus, everyone also gets a hernia. Fun game. May explain its popularity with the intelligentsia of Burbank and Newark.

AUTOMOBILE RACING: Your big chance to be a star. Everyone loves cars. And what with the grass, grit, noise, and probability that one or more of the participants will splatter themselves all over the nearest Dunlop sign, racing is understandably, unquestionably one of America's favorite spectator sports. That does not mean that it attracts more spectators than any other. Rather, its fans are so strung out on the spectacle of it all that they keep coming back to shower their champions with adulation, big money, and kisses from pretty girls again and again and again. The latter reward may cause something of a spectacle in itself whenever Janet Guthrie finally gets around to winning Indy, but that is another chapter. The point in play at the moment is: A rocket on wheels may be your ticket to the big time. To see if you have the keen instincts and nerves of steel it takes to lead the pack, simply head for the nearest theme park and ride its roller coaster with the longest waiting line three times in a row without a seat belt. Keep your cookies down and you ought to be a natural. In addition to your being dumb enough for the job, this will indicate that you have a sense of humor, which will come in handy if you decide to specialize in running funny cars.

GOLF: Game is a misnomer. A mortal test of endurance and mental stability comes closer to accuracy. Golf is one of the very few ostensibly athletic encounters in which no one throws a ball at you, kicks it at you, or tries ignominiously to jam it down your throat. Almost definitely the only one at which forty-year-olds are generally more proficient than teenagers. Certainly it is the sole competition that does not necessarily call for any competition and in which the winner gets the lowest score. Spectators and play-by-play commentators are expected to get excited very quietly, superstars wear pastel knickers and carry umbrellas, and the goal throughout the event, which is called a round, is to balance a dimpled ball the size of a plum on top of a toothpick, then to smack it squarely over several forests, oceans, marshes, coral reefs, mountains, valleys, beaches, and assorted other topographical nightmares into a total of eighteen buried coffee cups. Of course, none of that can happen until you learn how to lock rigidly most of your larger muscles in two directions at once and to weave the pinkie finger of your rear hand just right around the shaft of brassies, mashies, or niblicks without ever moving your head again. Shouldn't be all that difficult. The ball just sits there, waiting to be clobbered. If you are not too proficient at doing so, it often even smiles reassuringly when the ninety-pounder you have hired to lug your hundred-pound bag of clubs finds it in some clever hiding place. The game is golf. The setting is pastoral. The mood and pace are serene. The result is absolutely maddening. Tee it up at your own risk.

WIND SURFING: A real comer. Its recent popularity is probably due to the soft economy. All you need to play are an old ironing board, half a parachute, maybe an ocean, and a death wish.

BEER COMMERCIALS: A little bit of everything else and a barrel of laughs. Particularly great for seasoned veterans and other old guys because the average event lasts only about thirty seconds.

PINOCHLE AND SEX: Aficionados claim both to be in a virtual class with softball and bike riding. This, they say, is because they cannot be forgotten once learned and because there is nothing in the world of sports more demanding of one's killer instincts than a renege call or faked orgasm. I wouldn't know. I have never been able to tell pinochle from bridge, and what I don't know about sex could fill another chapter. Does so, in fact.

Other overlooked fun runs or jumps or whatevers with sizable followings include fishing (55 million people are said to enjoy squishing worms every year), motorcycling (35 million folks intent on proving themselves documentably crazier than car racers), ice skating (20 million despite Dick Button's best efforts), canoeing (5 or 6 million, counting kayakers, who are wet motorcyclists), and parachute jumping (200,000 and decreasing by the day). Now you tell me, how could a fancy survey with an iota of statistical validity miss fishing, canoeing, and parachuting?

Maybe these real winners were listed in a different part of the report. Sure hope so. The spotless reputation of one of the world's great scams is at stake here. A scandal could set Gallic-American relations back twenty years, and they cannot stand a whole lot of setting back.

So much for physical therapy. If we have not stumbled onto something that agitates your baser impulses by now, the answer lies elsewhere. In the arts perchance? A couple of pretty fair country demographers named Harris and Simmons think it a solid bet. In separate, possibly even more credible than Perrier studies, they concurred that somewhere in the neighborhood of 40 percent of all Americans (80 million, give or take a dozen or two) lean toward somewhat more creative outlets for their bottled juices. If true, artistic expression would rank as our second most common form of seltzerless relief. Again, selectivity is the key.

THE THEATER: If tramping the boards and projecting like crazy appeal, fear not. Fellow weekend thesbians abound. To connect with some in your vicinity, simply stand in any park or shopping mall reciting something moving and profound from *Please Don't Eat the Daisies* or *Jonathan Livingston Seagull*. Within three minutes you will be either arrested or invited to join the local chapter of the Little Repertory Players. As you probably know, all troupes of fellow weekend thesbians call themselves the Little Repertory Players. This has never been explained. Like fog and tank tops in San Francisco, it is just the way it is. Once inside the stage door, you will have your pick of introductory-level artsy-craftsy preoccupations. Painting scenery is a particularly safe way to break in because it is all but impossible for the naked eye to detect screwed-up clouds or bushes on poorly lit canvas from twenty feet. You will also find immediate openings in such relatively foolproof categories of subcreativity as concessions (translation: making popcorn) and house staff (translation: being an usher). Lighting, props, makeup, sound, and stage management are the next increasingly show bizzy steps within reasonable reach. Sell enough tickets, and you will eventually attain the ultimate honor of being asked to direct and/or of being cast for a speaking part in *The Matchmaker* by Otis Skinner or Amilia Earhart (I can never remember which). All local troupes of weekend thesbians called the Little Repertory Players present *The Matchmaker* by whoever it was by at least twice a year. This is also a mystery. Like high prices and henna in Miami Beach, it is just the way it is.

PAINTING: An adequate theatrical surrogate for less gregarious creatives. The only problem is it usually takes some talent. This can often be overcome by explaining you are in your surrealist period, but since growing a pointed mustache is not always such a snap, that also takes some degree of talent. Tell you what: Before investing in instruction books, color charts, palettes, brushes, paint, spirits, smocks, holes in the north side of your roof, and the like, take a trial run at a couple of those black velvet numbered jobs. If the sombrero and tiger come out looking like something they might hang in an A&P produce section or computer store foyer, by all means proceed. You could be the next Matisse. Speaking of whom, did I ever tell you the one about the time the New York Metropolitan Museum of Art hung one of his masterpieces upside down and no one noticed for six weeks? True story. Now that's art!

SCULPTING: Potentially excellent. Not only do a majority of sculpture's inspired observers have zero idea of what most objets d'art are supposed to be in real life anyway, but sculpture can almost definitely help you get rid of all the junk (*junque* to collectors; see ANTIQUING for exciting details) that has been growing and turning green in your garage since the last time you almost got around to cleaning it out. Paint cans and broken hoses, for instance, make far-out spiders and alien creatures. (That reminds me: Be sure also to check out the video game catalogue which follows.) Even if you keep a tidy garage, there is benefit to be had from hands on art. Smushing great globs of clay and flailing at things with hammers and blow-torches can be very therapeutic. Who knows, with more sculpting there could be less rheumatism and mental illness in the world; fewer garage sales at the very least.

MACRAMÉ: A bit kinky but okay because it ties (get it, didja, huh?) right into one of our most favorite nonathletic hobbies: indoor gardening (34 percent participation). Great memory jogger for old sailors and department store present wrappers. Also potentially lucrative for those lucky enough to live close to restaurants with cutesy names, cutesy menus, and cutesier food.

SINGING: Another big winner with executional opportunities aplenty. There are almost as many community Gilbert and Sullivan and barbershop societies as there are the Little Repertory Players troupes. There are even more church choirs and street-corner do-wop quintets. Worse comes to worst, there are showers almost every-where, and no singing is as satisfying or gratifying as shower singing . . . unless you are female, in which case you prefer the acoustics of a car.

DEBATING: Hardly as difficult an oddball penchant to vent as you might imagine. Ever hear of politics or flea markets?

CHESS: Yet another cinch. All it takes, according to Thomas J. Peters and Robert H. Waterman's runaway all-purpose business and corporate ego overloader *In Search of Excellence*, is the mental acu-men to project, to evaluate, and deftly to execute possible moves numbered at something on the order of 10 to the 120th power. By contrast, a trillion is far too many for clock face translation but a mere 10 to the 12th power. The fastest of modern-day computers can do something like 10 to the 20th sized calculations in about a cen-tury. As I said, a piece of cake.

Worth learning to play anyway if you live in or near Boston. This is because cultural Bostonians spend most of their free time sitting around commons or squares playing chess. They do so not because chess is such a big kick but because it is easier than learning how to talk funny and safer than trying to survive the area's kamikaze drivers.

Have you going? Sorry. Like belonging to great books clubs or wine tasting clubs, or getting all dressed up to be bored to death by operas and ballets, this fine arts business is all too nearly worth-while to qualify as legitimate off-hours frumping material. If you feel yourself getting cultural around the edges, suppress it as best you can on your own or get professional help. Try watching some television. Better yet, grab a few pounds of quarters and buy your-self some cold turkey withdrawal at a video game arcade.

A night at a video game arcade: Now there is a classic get-away-from-it-all idea. According to a recent Harvard study (Har-vard, for credibility's sake!), video games are better for you than all of Maria Montessori's large muscle development innovations with

Rubik's Cubes and throw rugs rolled into one. They are very contemporary as well. (You might be surprised by how few people old enough to remember Monopoly can rack up a measly score of 2 or 3 million on even the simplest of video games.) On top of all that, the obsession is extremely convenient to cultivate. For roughly a fourth of us, it does not even call for leaving the house. Through the miracle of Japanese technology, hundreds of thousands of middle-class American homes have been turned into fully equipped media centers in the last decade.

In addition to the ubiquitous Atari, there are videotape machines, wall-size projection screens, videodiscs, 100-channel cable services, self-actuated telephones, and honest to Dr. Strangelove personal computers plugged into every socket in sight. In the hearts and minds of users and sellers alike, video games come first. For the uninitiated, of which there may still be twelve out there somewhere in the universe, some of the one-eyed monster's more intriguing challenges to your manual dexterity and powers of hand-eye coordination are:

CENTIPEDE: Brightly colored caterpillars slither about the screen. The object is to exterminate them with electronic shots of insecticide triggered by a Freudian weapon called a joy stick before they exterminate you.

SPACE INVADERS: Brightly colored UFOs descend menacingly. The object is to obliterate them with electronic lazer beams triggered by your joy stick before they obliterate you.

ASTEROIDS: Brightly colored orbs flit perilously close to your stern and bow. The object is to pulverize them with electronic blasts from your omnipresent joy stick ray gun before they pulverize you.

Starting to get the picture? These cathode marvels are not only more fun than a week on Bourbon Street (big deal: An hour in Des Moines is more fun than a week on Bourbon Street if your tastes don't happen to run to female impersonators or muggers) but also absolutely accurate reflections of our current attitudes, values, and mores. Zap or be zapped. Above all else, do it with painless electronic wizardry. Something goes wrong, you can always punch the reset button and get a new lease on life.

There are, of course, an infinite number of less predictable permutations available at better discount stores and gas stations everywhere. Some actually call for skills other than blasting threatening objects out of the electronic sky. Neither of those supersellers Pac-Man and his gluttonously liberated counterpart Ms. Pac-Man, for unavoidable examples, require zapping of any kind. Hard as it may be to believe, they don't even involve the use of a joy stick. Rather, with the help of equally lethal implements called paddles, they blip frenetically around the screen, gobbling up brightly colored little guys with picket fence bellies. How's that for variety! As a historic aside with which to amaze and amuse your friends between hypnotic sessions, you might not have even realized it, but you knew these lovable gluttons long before you ever thrilled to their voracious profiles in action. Who do you suppose posed for all those yellow smile buttons a few years back? Hey, you gotta start somewhere.

And the fun doesn't stop there. Donkey Kong invites the brave of heart and quick of finger to relive one of the silver screen's timeless confrontations by saving an appropriately bulbous beauty from the clutches of that greatest of great apes himself. This is accomplished by directing a sledgehammer flomping carnival barker or corporate attorney (tough to tell) up an endless series of precarious ladders and over what look to be bowling balls the big guy has lobbed in his direction. Finally, victoriously, you get to help him clobber Kong right off his perch. Again, a good time had by all. Similarly, Frogger, Zartoc, Pitfall!, Night Driver, and approximately 12,000 others call for the negotiation of multidangered labyrinths of one kind or another to the incessant warbling praise of your friendly tube. Needless to say, we have come a long way since Pong. Makes you get all choked up, doesn't it?

The only documentable downer on the fabulous video game scene so far was the untimely demise of a wonderfully innovative paean to history's ultimate optimist. Custer or General George or Goldilocks and the Indians or whatever it was called had to be removed from the market because spoilsport do-gooders whined about its action-packed massacre, scalping, and rape sequences. Can you imagine negative thinkers having that much impact on how the rest of us get to dump our quarters in our own time? It's as though play value and the substantive increase of cognitive skills meant nothing to them. Enough to make W. Clement Stone frown, and that man frowned about as often as Halley's comet takes a pit stop. Especially sad when you realize the object of their disaffection was uniquely reflective of all that is good and true in our innermost collective psyche. Think about it. Where could you possibly find more concentrated Americana than in a single piece of space age technology that rolls sex, violence, and historic revisionism into one glorious two-bit blowout? Oh, sure, the game was trash. But it was one-of-a-kind trash in an age of microchip-precise goody-goodiness. No doubt about it, a terrible loss for generations of videophiles to come.

Well, can't win 'em all. Besides, it is not, as will become clear on the rest of our tour of the video room, as though we did not still have plenty of winking, blinking wonders immediately, addictively at hand.

Turn now from the tube to the computer terminal, and pause for a moment to consider how unlikely the entire concept of being able to do so really is. Until a couple of years ago *terminal* meant the Big C. Today it is but the breach of a brave new cybernetic world to come, a world in which you may never again have to leave the house to buy potatoes or see, smell, and feel the essence of faraway places. The amazing thing is we aren't talking science fiction tomorrowland tickets. The technology is here and now, and I, for one, don't know if I'm ready for it. Whereas the fact that roughly 25 percent of all Americans play one or more video games a day, every day, does not seem all that surprising to anyone who knows how much it costs to hire George Plimpton to do commercials and to run them on the Super Bowl (the Super Bowl, for ultimate experience's sake!), 6 or 7 percent of us actually puttering around with a personal computer just about as often blows me away. There are already 14 or 15 million family room "users" merrily blipping their way through tax forms and dungeons full of dragons and who knows what all. And there are millions more getting hooked by the minute. Unbelievable when you realize the things hardly existed this side of NASA or the FBI as recently as those halcyon days when Magruder, Dean, and Company were skulking their way into the history books.

Hooked is the only word that does justice to the typical home computer operator's mental state. Spending enraptured weeks learning how to initialize discs and months plowing through instruction manuals written in such exotic tongues as Integer and Pascal, these intrepid pioneers, armed only with keyboard and cursor, make all other forms of video freaks look like pikers. To their absolute delight, it usually takes them longer to master most user-friendly programs than people lived a century or two ago. This is to their absolute delight because there may be no feeling of accomplishment so profound as the production of one's first solo matrix dot printed grocery shopping list, no depression half as debilitating as that brought on by the first hashed file or purged memory bank. The highs are very high; the lows, damned near unbearable. Like golf, the results are consuming. A computer widow acquaintance of mine thought she was being snide when she asked her bleary-eyed, puffy-fingered husband if he thought there had been life before the Apple IIe. He said he did not know but doubted it. Justifiable homicide. No jury in the world would have convicted her, not yet anyway.

Fortunately, brainwashed members of fanatic bytes sects, like Moonies and leftover Mouseketeers, are still in the minority everywhere except airports and VisiCalc conventions. As long as the basic hardware and most of the trickier software remain in the three-figure cost category, the rest of us will probably be safe. Should take about three months. Suffice to say, sooner or later, we shall be a race of computerspeak Trons. In the meantime, the leading leisure grabbers are likely to continue to be:

Watching TV
Listening to radio or music
Going to movies
Sports spectating
Reading (surprise)
Participating in sports
Doing outdoor gardening
Driving cars
Collecting
Doing indoor gardening
Cooking
Playing table or lawn games
Doing needlework
Travel
Pets
Children
Miscellaneous

The participation stats were intentionally left out because their order as shown is a compilation of several different surveys and the footnotes would have taken longer to digest than an introductory IBM manual. Trust me on this one.

Sitting in front of a television set is, of course, not so much a way to relax as it is practice for being dead. The average adult spends about forty hours a week staring at the thing. The average child puts in approximately forty hours a day. What usually stares back defies description. The last decade's top series included "Laverne and Shirley," "The Love Boat," "Fantasy Island," "Dynasty," "Benny Hill," and "Three's Company." I rest my case. I do so knowing full well it will have the effect of a cork on Mount St. Helens. You will go right on staring. So shall I. But please, for your own good and that of those you love, get up every once in a while for potato chips. Otherwise, you may be gone for an entire season of cancellations before anyone notices that you were one of the cancellations.

There are, to be fair, exceptions to the general rule of offensive TV fare. They are named "Hill Street Blues"; "M*A*S*H" reruns; "Monty Python's Flying Circus" (which was in rerun over there before it was ever in first run here); most other BBC discards; "Good Morning America"; "The Today Show"; Johnny Carson; David Letterman; Phil Donahue; and "AM [insert a city]." Actually, only the first couple live up to the billing, but what with the possibility of having to hit the circuit, I figured it couldn't hurt to say something nice about the rest. Oh, "Cosby" and "Newhart" are good too.

Listening to radio or to music from some other source comes in at about the same usage levels—somewhere in the high nine-tieth percentile. They are not, however, as potentially harmful as most other electro-media addictions because both inactivities normally allow for a wide variety of simultaneous pursuits. You can, for instance, clip toenails or build toothpick skyscrapers while doing either. Be careful anyway. Certain kinds of radio are capable of actually making you think. (Yes, baby boomers, there is still life on the AM dial.) This is potentially dangerous. If subjected to its impact too often, you could develop a serious case of awareness, which would automatically disqualify you from the happy hour club you are trying to join. Not worth the risk. Move on to something more legitimately idle before it is too late.

Try taking in a flic. Nowhere, not even in an evening with "That's Incredible" or the network superstars in gym shorts, is time more deliciously wasted or our true subconscious orientation more clearly mirrored than at the movies. The patterns have changed some over the years. Films (as movies are known to the *auteur* crowd) now come to us as often as we go to them, but on whole, we still enjoy the 70-mm Dolby accentuated brand of escape more than almost anything. And those escapes we enjoy the most speak reams about us. Unfortunately what they say isn't always exactly complimentary, but then neither are most mothers-in-law.

The odds of a movie's making it where it counts, at the cash register, seem directly proportional to the amount of maiming, cheating, laser zapping, and/or unencumbered skin it has to offer. At the top of the all-time box-office winners' list: the *Star Wars* trilogy. To be honest, an arguably alien notion in context of a discussion of accepted tinseltown accounting procedures, no one can even imagine how much they have made to date. A couple of billion seems a reasonable guess. No, that was not a typo. It was supposed to be a B (as in *billion*) not an M (as in *modest return on investment*). If not, it was at least enough to give George Lucas a BMW and me a chance to prove how far a nothing premise can be milked. No matter how you add it up, the bigger-than-life exploits of Luke and Leia and company made a bunch of money. Legitimately deserved reward for unparalleled cinematic virtues and wholesome family fun? Horsefeathers or, in the clever code of yet another exciting chapter to come (in the biz, such tease lines are called trailers . . . see how much you are learning here), $#!+. Between doses of oblique philosophy, *Wars, Empire,* and *Jedi* (in the great tradition of John Wayne and Robin Hood) first and foremost provide a steady stream of long-ago and faraway blood and guts. Erector set dinosaurs stomp on cute little teddy bears. Cruisers, fighters, and death stars splatter all over the place in special effects splendor that would do ColecoVision proud. Good guys neon-sword bad guy's arms off at the elbow. Flying motorcycle jockeys smash into endangered trees. Slimy creatures gulp each other down and snort grotesque potions while animated chess pieces crunch their way from square to square. A monk and a muppet (mygawd, a monk and a muppet!) teach some nice young kid how to zap his own father, a duper villain who just happens to enjoy wearing flowing black gowns and pharaohs' masks all day long, with a—you guessed it—electronic joy stick. Don't get me wrong. They are outstanding entertainments. They are also, however, what they are—pretty gross. If that is your emotional cookie, fine. Recognize it, or you will wind up on the couch. You may do so anyway, but you will at least know why going in, which will save lots of your and the good doctor's valuable time, which could obviously be better spent at the movies.

Distinctly antisocial behavior permeates most of the rest of the bonafide celluloid biggies as well.

Jaws: What have we got so far? Eighty or ninety New England teenyboppers and their sailboats munched by rampaging fish?

The Godfather epics triggered lines around the block for months waiting to watch half of the fedora wearers this side of Cal City get rat-a-tat-tatted all over the nearest toll booth; a real tough guy named Sonny whip his pregnant wife with a belt; Marlon Brando win the honor of refusing to accept an Oscar for choking on wads of cotton; and some other top tutti roll over and hug a decapitated horse.

Close Encounters of the Third Kind featured these cuddly little aliens that had a habit of kidnapping earthlings and shutting down monuments in the name of intergalactic harmony.

Moving right along, we find a Bogart clone (Han Solo in mufti) playing a happy-go-lucky archaeologist who rolls them in the aisles by tossing Nazis into airplane propellers when he isn't rummaging for biblical memorabilia in overcrowded snake pits; a perpetually grinning good ol' boy (Burt, of course) smashing a car a minute; a stoic big-city cop (Burt's best buddy Clint) sticking his cannon into creeps' mouths while trying to keep count of his bullets; a more or less reformed hit man named Rocky (if your real name were Sylvester, you would have probably learned how to swallow raw eggs, too) bashing faces, including his own, into pulps every time he needs to make a comeback because of some dud in which he makes the fatal mistake of trying to speak as well as grunt; and a credit crawl full of like heroes and alternately skimpily clad or tough-talking heroines emoting each other into boffo legend. And that doesn't even take into account the profitable grade B legions of rampaging insects/rampaging madman/rampaging horny teenager genre smashes that rake it in year after year.

Even our consensus "most loved" film, *Gone with the Wind*, was a thinly veiled soaper with innards squirting out of every other frame. Remember the train station? Remember Atlanta? Give a damn? Frankly, my dear, neither would I if not to make the point that mayhem sells more jujubes than Disney retreads ever have or ever will. The sole alleged exception, *E.T.*, was obviously a figment of your imagination. For proof, consider his penchant for Reese's Pieces. Self-respecting candy counters do not push Reese's Pieces. They push grease-drenched popcorn and rock-coated almonds and other things patrons won't have so much trouble holding down while watching someone throw up in *The Exorcist XXCII.* (Sequels are bankable, you know.)

None of this is intended as indictment. Don't be shy about your subliminal preferences. If your idea of a big time in the great outdoors is a six-pack at the drive-in, go for it. With the exceptions of those by Ingmar Bergman, movies move. Of course, so do bowels.

No such problem of psychological disorientation plague the sports fan. A seat on the fifty or the third-base line or midcourt or wherever else you have to hock the jewels to sit is a license to act as violently out of control as you care to without so much as a questioning glance from anyone around you. That is because everyone around you will also be raising pent-up emotion by pounding each other on the back and screaming hysterically over the gravity-defying exploits of interchangeable ghetto kids turned instant millionaires whom they have never met and never will and to whom they would probably have nothing to say beyond "Uh, could I have your autograph for my, uh, mother?" if they ever did. Psychologists say one of the most interesting facets of this frenzied spectating phenomenon is that fans actually cheer less for the players than they do for their uniforms. Like most things psychologists say, this fact is not only interesting but also utterly irrelevant. Establishing meaningful personal relationships is not the primary goal of going to weekly games of the century. People go by the millions to have a good time. And they do. What with the occasional fresh air, indigestible hot dogs, and camaraderie of equally rabid total strangers on every side, you just cannot beat fun at the old ball park or stadium or other ugly building with the dumb name and clock in the shape of a can of beer. Heck, it is even moderately amusing to pray for the Cubs.

Definitely give this one a try. If your level of insecurity is such that you might feel uncomfortable breaking new ground on your own, here are the ceremonial forms of titanic struggle everyone else has decided are the most fun to spectate either in person or through the vicarious magic of the tube:

1. Pro football
2. College football
3. Major-league baseball
4. College basketball
5. Pro basketball
6. Pro tennis
7. Boxing
8. Golf
9. Auto racing
10. Soccer

Yeah, car racing being that low and pro round ball being that high and horse racing being nowhere at all surprised me, too. So, for that matter, did the omissions of rugby (which features one really exciting formation, called the scrum line, in which small guys on each team stick their heads through the arms of big guys and are used as battering rams) and bullfighting (a model of efficiency in which preparation of the vendors' hot dogs center ring is the big attraction). But turnstiles do not lie, not usually anyhow. Learning such things is, I suppose, why most people who are not receptionists in real life read books. (Reading books is part of receptionists' official job description, so they do not count.) It is also, I suppose, a few inches to the left of center at the moment. We were trying to help you get started at being a big fan of some sport by helping you pick some sport to be a fan of. No sweat. Well, considering the size of crowds attending most games of the century, hardly any sweat.

Getting started is simple. Next time you see 20,000 cars trying to squeeze into a single line, get in line. Something worth spectating is probably about to happen, and the odds are it will be something athletic in nature. Of course, it could also be the Police or Stevie Nicks in Concert or a bunch of poor souls on their way to work. Better scratch plan A. Plan B is fail-safe. Wait until you see an ad for some event at which the San Diego Chicken is scheduled to be totally insane. The Chicken guarantees a good time even if you wind up hating sports. For best results, regardless of setting, wear a "Jesus Saves" T-shirt and multicolored Afro wig. This will get you on television and make you an immediate lower-case legend in your own rite.

The next entry on the list, reading, is, as parenthetically noted, a real shocker. I frankly didn't realize it was still in such widespread vogue. If you know how to do it, and this meaningful shared experience does seem to point in that general direction, go ahead. Optometrists will love you, and at the very least, it will be worth a good laugh or two when you peek over the cover to see your friends' looks of abject disbelief. Classics or poetry would be far too much like work, but otherwise, what you read is pretty much your call. Here, too, following the example of those more experienced in the avocation is acceptable strategy. Although they almost invariably deny it when asked in public (status conferral at its most insidious), a vast majority of present-day literati stick to pulp with occasional detours through newspapers, magazines, and even full-length paperbacks. Workingwomen (60-some percent of the gender, as of the last census count) are the most avid and frequent readers. Without their patronage, most pharmacies would be belly up in a month and the administration's merry band of handpicked conservationists would have to think up some other reason to wipe out forests.

Again, proceed at risk to your laggard standing. What begins with an innocent Victorian romance or Agatha Christie could all too subtly evolve into a hard-core current events habit or, perish the thought, serious literature monkey before you realize what is going down. Once Vonnegut hits your nightstand, Conrad may not be far behind.

Any more on bailout number six, sports participation, would be overkill, so let's dig into number seven on the list, outdoor gardening. Do not worry about the bends or any other withdrawal symptoms. Gardening strains many of the same muscles as jocking and comes in almost as many thoroughly punishing varieties. Whether you choose heavy-duty landscaping, backyard farming, or decorative pansy bedding, two basic aptitudes are crucial to getting the most out of the experience. Most green things have horticultural surnames that run off the edge of the average page, and planting any one of them takes some digging. That means the would-be gardener must enjoy scraping dirt out of fingernails and pretending he or she understands Latin. If you are the meticulous type or a Berlitz dropout, take a pass.

Driving cars comes in eighth. It should not come in anywhere on this particular set. Automobiles are not hobbies. They are lovers. Even in the wake of the bogus energy crisis and resultant model crunch, America's affair with the car goes on and on and on. As long as you do not mind the idea of contributing to assorted sheikhs' retirement funds once or twice a week, join the club. Having someone, er, something to bathe, lubricate, and ignite whenever you get the urge is not all bad.

Ninth and coming on fast is collecting. A big part of its charm is a total lack of rules. Anything and everything can be fair game for the avid collector. Redundant phrase. Sorry. All collectors, regardless of specific affliction, are avid by definition. Some roll string into tremendous balls. Others pile lifetime supplies of *National Geographics* into minutely detailed cross-reference heaps. Volunteer firemen in the more remote suburbs say the last smoking embers are usually what is left of a *National Geographic* collection. Many flit from bottle caps to bubble gum cards to matchbook covers and back again with equal fervor. Rich collectors do cars. Some get so carried away they have to build ornate garages and call them museums to pay for the habit. By far the two most significant subcategories of the species collect stamps and antiques. Philatelists, as members of the sticky tongue set are known, enjoy fits of ecstasy over an unlicked commemorative with the palm fronds pointed against the prevailing winds or the monarch's eyes crossed. As a group and individually, antiquers are capable of comparable or greater giddiness when allowed into someone's attic alone. They are also easy to pick out in a crowd. It's their eyes.

They dilate to four times normal size at the sight of dented furniture and roll in their sockets on contact with musty odors. Perhaps the nicest thing about their *junque* fetish is that it works to the advantage of regular people who would either have junk piled to the rafters or be forced to take up sculpting. At this tender stage of compulsion, don't get too hung up on picking the perfect treasure to save. Sometime when you least expect it, something will pick you. It may be a strange-looking button or a campaign poster or a street sign. Whatever it is, you will know it, and you will want every one in existence for your very own.

We have already touched upon the next most preferred time waster, indoor gardening. Its primary distinctions from the outdoor variety are smaller shovels and, in extreme cases, the remodeling of its practitioners' homes into tropical rain forests. Dirty nails and the need to converse with fellow enthusiasts in a dead language remain the primary hazards to be overcome. One of its definitely underrated advantages is the ability it confers to graduate from conifers and get into some of the really exotic action. Tough to sprout Venus's flytraps on the patio, you know. That is a shame. The patio is where you could really use one.

Requiring proficiency in every skill in the book and providing its proponents the hands-down most immediately gratifying payoff, cooking deserves a better call than it apparently gets. Cooking is art. Cooking is science. Cooking is sport. Cooking is hobby. Cooking is passion and style and panache. Cooking thrills, delights, frustrates, terrorizes, and even keeps otherwise presumably talentless individuals with funny voices in childlike euphoria by the hour. Yet here it sits in a virtual tie with sticking your hands in dirt (okay, sticking your hands in humus and mulch) as a way to have a good time. Hard to figure why only 32 or 33 percent of adults seem to consider culinary expertise to be one of their favorite off-hours activities. Must have something to do with the fact that the other 150 million or so of us are at least peripherally involved in doing it for a living. I can see how that would take some of the fun out of it.

In any event, cooking comes so highly recommended by those who dig it (instead of dirt or humus or mulch or other things that can get under your fingernails) that you would be silly not at least to give it a try. Besides, it is such a snap it won't cost you much to get started. To do so, all you will need is a pot, some meat, a fire, water, a dash of pepper, and a pinch of salt. Once procured, assemble and utilize these ingredients as follows:

STEP 1. Light the fire.
STEP 2. Put the meat in the pot.
STEP 3. Put the pepper and salt on the meat.
STEP 4. Put the pot on the fire.
STEP 5. Wait until the meat changes color, then take it out of the pot and eat it.
STEP 6. Use half of the water to put out the fire and the other half to wash out the pot. Be sure to do this in this order as trying to wash the pot before putting out the fire can burn your fingers.

Helpful hints for the beginner:

1. If the meat has already changed color while you were trying to start the fire, do not eat it until someone has had a taste.
2. Be sure to look at and smell the meat as it burns. Eye and nose appeal is an important part of the overall cooking experience.
3. If water is not available, sand or beach blankets may be substituted for those parts of the recipe that call for it.
4. When both water and either sand or beach blankets are available, use one or both of the latter to extinguish the fire and pour the water into the pot. Depending upon how long it takes your meat to change color, you will then have either soup or gravy to go with it.
5. Buy your pepper and salt in chunks; then grind them as you go. While this will not do anything in particular to their taste, it will make you look very big time.

If you follow these simple instructions and tips exactly as issued, you will be an official cook and, as such, qualified to fill your belly as the need arises. Not necessarily, however, to enrich your soul. That calls for being a chef. Since enriching your soul was one of the assignments that sent us off on this tangent in the first place, a chef is something worth being. To become one, master the basics of cooking (especially Point 5); then develop a flair for flipping the meat out of the pot a special way or dowsing the fire while turning in circles and whistling. Lastly, buy a mushroom-shaped hat, a bib apron with something witty written on it, several long forks, and a book on cuisine. As you no doubt already know, cuisine is what people call cooking from somewhere else. The same principle applies to what people call experts. People usually ignore it when some mope from down the block gets on his soapbox. Same guy gives the same speech in Topeka, and they line up for tickets and invite him to be on talk shows. (I do not know why this is so. Like Osmond-shaped noses and polygamy in Salt Lake City, it is just the way it is.) Tell you what: As a bonus, I shall give you all the tips you will need for the cuisine part of your chef training right here. With the money you save by not having to buy a book on the subject, you can go back to wherever you lifted this one and pay for it if you like it so far. If not, you can buy some more meat.

GOURMET (cuisine type) Recipes for Meat in a Pot with Salt and Pepper

A LA FRANÇAISE: Replace the water with wine or cream or both.
ESPAÑOL: Toss in some jalapeño peppers and a can of beans.
ANGLAISE: Pour all the water into the pot (let someone else worry about putting out the fire) and cook until the meat is absolutely tasteless.
O'SHAMROCKY: Add potato.
RUSSKY: Add a beet.
ORIENTALE: Add bean sprouts.
ITALIENNE: Add one tomato and forty-six cloves of fresh garlic.
POLSKI: Add noodles.
DER VATERLAND: Add a head of cabbage, click your heels, and salute the pot.

MAGYAR: Add paprika and pigs' feet.

NEW DELHI STYLE: Take out the meat, and show it some respect.

GRECO: Add olives, and ask your handkerchief to dance around the pot.

AMAZONIAN: Tenderize the meat by shooting it with blow darts before burning.

AMÉRICAINE: Time out! A tough one. We are such a diverse and multicultured nation that no single adaptation could possibly do us justice. Hence a potpourri of regional favorites:

AMERICAN (gourmand type) Recipes for Meat in a Pot with Pepper and Salt

NORTH STAR STYLE (a Minneapolis-St. Paul favorite): Add wild rice and wear a Viking helmet as you serve.

LA CREOLE STYLE (from Cajun Country): Pretend you are cooking, oops, pretend you are chefing Italian, and use shrimp meat and as much okra as you can find at the store.

MANHATTAN STYLE (no doubt a redundancy in some circles): Treat the ingredients rudely. Punch anyone who asks for a taste.

CHESAPEAKE BAY STYLE (a Baltimore delicacy): Cook it any way you wish. Eat everything, including the pot. Move to Indianapolis.

GOLDEN GATE STYLE: Use mincemeat, and beat it before you eat it.

LOS ANGELENO: Discard the meat, salt, and pepper. Use Perrier water. Add sprouts and avocado curd. Eat cold with your legs crossed.

BEVERLY HILLS STYLE: Serve the above on solid gold plates, and garnish with uncooked flour or more readily available powder substitute.

DOWN EASTERLY: Scald a live lobster and several rocks with rubber bands living inside them. Mix well with the sand and beach blanket before eating.

NEBRASKA STYLE: Serve with no less than six kinds of corn side dishes and a Nehi.

HAWAIIAN: Add a pineapple and some mushed raw fish.

BRAISED IN BLUEGRASS: Use out-of-the-money horsemeat, and add a sprig of mint.

CHICAGO STYLE: Throw away the pot, and burn the meat in a deep-dish pan.

BIG D BARBECUE STYLE: Take one entire cow; hang it on a rotating stick directly over the fire; baste with gallons of chili sauce and Lone Star beer until the color into which it turns is black. Shout "whoopee" or "whoa, boy" every once in a while jest to git the pot's attention.

WHEN AND HOW TO SERVE

If it is morning, replace the water with prune juice, and add an egg. Yawn and scratch intermittently.

If it is midday, do not bother. Finish off whatever you burned the preceding evening on a piece or two of bread with mayo.

If it is dinnertime, pound the meat with a hammer before putting it in the pot. This will enhance the effect by creating the optical illusion of larger portions.

If it is Thanksgiving or Christmas, use only dead-bird meat and bake cookies.

If it is summer, eat watermelon instead.

If it is two in the morning, resist the urge to have a cigarette! when you are finished.

For further information, consult someone's grandmother. Grandmothers know more about cooking than anyone.

Surprisingly this brings us to the bottom of the double-digit column. Surprising at first blush because the next on the list is needleworking. Surprising upon closer observation because it ends without a word about pets or children. Since I know less about needleworking than I do about pinochle or sex and do not care to learn, we shall proceed briskly to travel, pets, and children, about each of which I am either personally expert or entirely capable of fudging.

Travel: Can you believe they did not log travel higher? Even if only over the river, past nine Stuckeys, and through the woods to

Grandma's house, everyone enjoys traveling. There are three basic types worth noting: business travel for pleasure, foreign vacations, and domestic vacations. Business travel for pleasure: A contradiction in terms. Reject. Make that two basic types worth noting: foreign vacations and domestic vacations. In many ways they are quite similar. Both require several hundred pounds of camera equipment, clothing you would never be caught dead in near home, and, most important, breathtaking amounts of money. In many other ways they are distinct. Foreign vacations necessitate shots and cannot normally be done by automobile unless you count Canada and Mexico as foreign countries. As long as the itinerary does not include St. Louis, domestic vacations (which indicates how unlikely it is that the itinerary will include St. Louis) call for no medical punctures and can easily be done by automobile unless you count Hawaii, Puerto Rico, and New York City as parts of this country. Their biggest difference is, of course, the respective kinds of travelers, or tourists, as they are called in the trade, who do them. As they will readily tell you in case they think you have not noticed, foreign tourists are a sophisticated lot given to knowing the meaning of such international phrases as *concierge* and *in season*. They need no help from me in conceiving their next exotic escapade. Domestic tourists, on the other hand, are usually more familiar with currency exchanges than currency conversions and sensible enough to take all the help they can get. My kinds of folks. For them, a miniatlas of recommended fun spots within the natural, albeit probably once arbitrarily scribbled, borders of our connected forty-eight. Lest you get the impression it is some kind of knee-jerk idea to fill a couple of pages before we get back to the good part, I'll have you know it took years of intensive eavesdropping in Holiday Inn parking lots to compile. Have any notion of how difficult it is to eavesdrop intensely in a Holiday Inn parking lot without having a "Virginia Is for Lovers" or "Go Hike the Canyon" bumper sticker pasted onto your forehead? Takes stealth, dedication, and a strange sense of how to have a good time, I assure you.

DISNEYLAND, DISNEY WORLD, EPCOT CENTRE (which you can tell immediately is a pretty big deal by the way it is spelled): Absolute musts for those with children; better yet for those without them. As the brochures advise, if you can take only one vacation this year, make it to one or two or all of these literally magic kingdoms. With just the slightest squint, they can double for everywhere else anyway. They even have their own alphabetized currency and public transportation systems. Shame they cannot figure out a way to do something about their rodent and stray animal problems, though. The darned things walk right up to you on the street and start chatting like old pals. Some actually volunteer to have their pictures taken with you. Still, the rest of the package is so outstanding it is definitely worth the hassle.

Reachable only by monorail or parking lot tram.

Travel planner tips: Wear comfortable shoes, as they are larger than some other countries; wear deodorant, as they are in temperate climates and usually crowded; and bring along *War and Peace*, as you will spend most of your visit standing in lines with nothing much to do.

ASPEN, COLORADO: The man with the squeaky voice and rose-colored glasses sure knew what he was talking about when he dubbed it the home of Rocky Mountain highs. Great scenery. Great music. Plenty of powder on and off the slopes the year around. How can you lose?

Can be arrived at by plane, car, chair lift, or mule.

Be sure to wear authentic cowboy shirts and boots so the locals will know you are a tourist and treat you with respect.

LAS VEGAS: Glitter Gulch, as it is known to everyone this side of Atlantic City, is the power company's favorite place in the entire world. Its attractions include twenty-four hours of daylight every day of the year; big name and/or big boob cabaret shows; gaming to your heart's desire or credit limit, whichever comes first; the on-call services of innumerable platinum-haired entertainment directors; and, for excitement, side trips to Hoover Dam. Since this oasis of the good life is owned and operated by large gentlemen whose surnames end in vowels, it also offers broken kneecaps or worse to those who play first and fail to pay later.

Most easily reached by almost-all-expenses-paid three-day charter.

Prepare yourself by staying up all night for at least two months before leaving home. Bring money.

NEW ORLEANS: Sort of a grubby Disneyland. Justifiably famous for its restaurants, funerals, and a pleasure strip named after booze which has somehow managed, presumably unnoticed by the city fathers and mothers, to slip from raunchy to sleazy and repulsive. Great spot if you don't mind occasionally odd smells in the morning air.

You can get there by Mississippi paddle-wheeler, which is pretty sexy, but somehow, Greyhound bus seems more appropriate.

Pack noseplugs.

TUSCALOOSA, ALABAMA: I have never been to Tuscaloosa, Alabama. I do not know anyone who has ever been to Tuscaloosa, Alabama. It does, however, have such a terrific name that I had to squeeze it in somehow. Frankly, I don't know how you might go about getting there. Since there can't be all that much to do somewhere no one I know has ever been, this is probably okay.

THE BIG APPLE: New Orleans with taller buildings and meaner cabdrivers. The hookers are about even.

Attainable only by birth, which explains why the natives are always in such a bad mood, or by climbing corporate ladders, which explains why the newcomers always look so tired.

WASHINGTON, D.C.: The rarest of the rare. A place that comes close to exceeding expectations. All the more amazing when you consider the transiency of its population and the fact that all there is to look at is a bunch of buildings and statues and pieces of old parchment.

Can best be reached by the campaign trail or electoral college.

THE GRAND CANYON: Of course. This ain't your normal, everyday hole in the ground, you know. Full of rocks that change colors and photogenic donkeys, it is one of the world's great natural wonders and must be seen in person at dawn to be appreciated.

YELLOWSTONE: Sure, why not? This ain't your normal, everyday steambath, you know. Full of automatic geysers and photogenic bears, it is one of the world's great natural wonders and must be seen in person at dawn to be appreciated.

THE EVERGLADES: Definitely. This ain't your normal, everyday mud puddle, you know. Full of green things with Latin names and photogenic alligators, it is one of the world's great natural wonders and must be seen in person at dawn to be appreciated.

GREAT SMOKY MOUNTAINS: Unfortunately all the smoking they do makes them impossible to appreciate at dawn in person, but the National Park Service would not have endorsed their great natural wonders if they didn't have something pretty special going for them somewhere beneath the haze. I have heard it is called Knoxville.

Why don't you just take their word for it and plan to hit all the nice places they designate as being among the world's great natural wonders and save me some paper here? There are about 150 parks or monuments or whatever scattered around the countryside. You ought to be able to make the circuit before overcrowding or pollution or the government's environmental protection policies do them in.

MARS: Not yet but sooner than you think. NASA is already accepting reservations for turn-of-the-century shuttles in case you hadn't heard.

BOSTON: Heaven for academic and history buffs. The first college football game was played right down the road, you know.

SAN FRANCISCO: Okay now that the cable cars are fixed again. There was instant old in them thar hills for a while.

SOUTH DAKOTA: Washington, D.C., with trees.

Other places. Whatever. Sounds good to me. Sounds even better to my brother-in-law. He's a travel agent. Well, he says he is going to be a travel agent. Right now he is in training. He sits around watching buses at the station. Fun guy.

That ought to keep you going for a while. Speaking of which, don't forget to take along the Kaopectate. All water is not created equal, and nothing, but nothing, can flush fun out of a holiday faster than being on the run when you are on the run.

No such problems with pets. If anything, psychiatrists, gerontologists, prison wardens, and like authorities seem convinced that dependent creatures' relationship to physiological disorder is more curative than causal. So much so they have actually begun recruiting furry assistants to help calm down, to pep up, and otherwise positively to alter their charges' mental states. Not exactly twenty-first-century thinking but not all bad. Not all bad at all. In point of simple fact, pets can do wonders for the human psyche. This is apparently because they are color-blind, have trouble remembering their companions' social status or IQ, and like to be patted on the head. Perhaps most important, their powers are not restricted to the old, the addled, or the incarcerated. Many regular people seem to enjoy them all the time.

Picking a little buddy or not so little buddy to match your tastes in playmates is not too tough. Generally (translation: erroneously) speaking, dogs are for men. Cats are for women. Birds are for apartment dwellers. Snakes are for weirdos. Rodents are for weirdos who own snakes and for kids who enjoy scaring the hell out of their mothers by asking, "Ma, you seen Herbie anywhere?" It should be noted that young people who enjoy Boy George are beyond the remedial range of pet therapy.

Choosing the perfect breed within the perfect species is trickier. Takes more thought than we have time to give it at the moment. There are, however, some fairly quick criteria to balance against your projected emotional needs. Let's start with mutts. Almost everyone does.

DOBERMAN PINSCHERS: They are said to be very smart and have character. This means they can kill you and get away with it by pleading temporary insanity. Dobie owners are a little strange. They cut off the beasts' ears, toes, and tails when they are puppies, then wonder why they grow up snarly.

FRENCH POODLES: Very bright, good at tricks, excellent for circus acts and hairdressing salons. Rumored not to be as wimpy as people make them look.

GERMAN SHEPHERDS: Good at guarding lumberyards, sniffing cocaine stashes, walking blind people across streets, and imitating Dobermans. That last part wasn't fair. Shepherds hardly ever kill their owners. They chew their arms and feet off once in a while but hardly ever kill.

RETRIEVERS: Good for people who lose things.

TERRIERS: Adept at standing on their hind legs, barking at fences, and following yellow brick roads.

CHIHUAHUAS: These are not dogs. They are rodents.

XOLOIZCUINTLI (does that look plural to you?): Don't have a clue, but you have to admit they have a great name. Just think how much fun you could have learning how to call one home for dinner or telling the mailcarrierperson what it is that just bit him or her.

WHIPPETS: Kinky little beasts. Like to wear leather collars around the house.

COCKER SPANIELS: Cute little buggers. Said to have a thing for whippets. Isn't that always the way?

BASSET HOUNDS: Walter Matthau look-alikes. They make nice paperweights and doorstops.

Cats are second in popularity everywhere except Broadway, where dogs don't usually do anywhere near as well. Can't imagine why. But then, the only cats with whom I am personally acquainted are Morris, Sylvester, and Garfield, all of whom are probably atypical because they can afford to be on the nip most of the time. Near as I can tell, everyday cats, regardless of pedigree, have these tendencies in common:

1. They act as though their stuff doesn't stink.
2. They are wrong.
3. They do not come home to visit very often, but when they do, they usually bring nice presents like partial mice.
4. They are sneaky.
5. They are very good at playing with balls of yarn, purring, fighting, and fornicating.
6. They get stuck in trees.
7. They have eight lives too many.

8. Their family names all sound as if they should belong to expensive rugs.

Birds are better: not a whole lot better but better. Mostly they are small and do not mind sitting around in relatively low-maintenance cages, making okay noises. Some are also colorful and charming conversationalists. The favorites:

PARAKEETS AND BUDGIES: While their proponents proclaim all manner of wondrous accomplishments, their two provable credentials are cheap purchase price and ease of disposal. They are flushable.

CANARIES: Tweet pleasantly and go well with most curtains.

FINCHES: Low-class canaries. Make good cat food.

MYNAS: Do great Don Rickles impersonations.

CHICKENS: Good with mashed potatoes.

PARROTS: Big suckers. Almost invariably hooked with twenty-cracker-a-day habits.

CROWS: They scare easily.

EAGLES: Make terrific national symbols.

COCKATOOS: Aristocratic, beautiful, smelly.

TURKEYS: Fun for kindergarteners to draw in school.

After these big three, all bets are off. Reptiles, monkeys, and rabbits belong in zoos. Fish, especially baby carp, are relatively peaceful to look at but expensive because they eat everything that fits into the bowl, including each other. Cows and horses are too messy. Forgive the presumption. Since the best pets offer protection as well as companionship, I recommend Wookies.

There is one fascinating sidebar to the pet parade. People supposedly get to looking and acting like their furry friends before too long. Or is it the other way around? Either way choose well.

Wouldn't want to wind up reminding casual acquaintances of Walter Matthau, would you? Still, you really should try to have something in common with the little fella. Start by going into the bathroom and listening to see if you are best at barking, meowing, hissing, or tweeting.

If the answer comes up "screaming at the top of your lungs," you don't need a pet. You need children. Contrary to what you might have heard, they are not the same. Pets are lovable; children are expensive. Pets are loyal; children run away, marry bums, and forget your birthday. Pets are satisfied with chew bones; children want bicycles. Just kidding. About the kids, too. Nothing else like them in the entire world. Nothing close. If you are lucky, have some the regular way. If not, have some any way you can. Whether by stork, red tape, or Bunsen burner, children make everything else in life, even work, worthwhile. They hug. They kiss. They laugh. They make it okay to play with dolls and electric trains. They provide a captive audience for all the wisdom you have managed to store over the years. They love. Best of all, they help you stay young while making you feel old.

The rest of our emotional placebos fall in the single-digit popularity category. This doesn't make them all bad or anything— merely selective. Do not let peer pressure dampen your enthusiasm if one of them seems to press your hot button. Individuality is a solid trait. Look what it did for Wink Martendale! Bad example, try again. Look what it did for Miss Piggy! That's better. Had she been willing to settle for a permanent gig in the chorus line, she would be bacon by now. Not her style. She saw what she wanted and went for it without giving so much as a second thought to what the rest of the porkers might be whispering around the pen. Take her lead. Set your sights on what's right for you, and do not settle for less unless you change your mind. It isn't as though you will exactly be alone on your limb regardless of the kind of work you decide to call play. Something appealing to only one-half of 1 percent of the population, which is not so coincidentally the approximate level of acceptance most of the also-rans attain, still has more fans than you could cram into the ten largest stadia in the country combined. Prediction. You will have company.

Suffice to say, there are as many outlets as you can imagine and several thousand more. Here, in nothing approaching order, consequence, or entirety, is one last, I promise, smattering of pump primers:

PLAYING TABLE GAMES: These venerated ancestors of the video generation seem to be holding their own very nicely, thank you. Monopoly is still the best, Parcheesi still the one with the most intriguing name, poker still the most expensive, and Yahtzee still the dumbest. Snooker does not count. Like Ping-Pong and backgammon, it is more a sport than a game. Games are fun. Sports are business.

PLAYING LAWN GAMES: Forget it. Jarts are dangerous. Boccie hurts your back. No one plays croquet anymore. This is as it should be. Grass is for freaky teenagers and fertilizer, not for widgets.

TAKING OVER the entire world in the guise of building landscapes for your electric trains.

TROLLING for women.

TROLLING for men.

TROLLING for one or more of each.

BUILDING THINGS: A tool shed might be a good start. Making it will give you something to do with the tools you will eventually store in it and will also allow for the therapeutic release of a colorful verbal litany. Boats in bottles are nice, too.

POLISHING SHOES: Helps you remember the good old days in boot camp. This, in turn, helps prove that absolutely any period of your life can and will be remembered as "the good old days" once you don't have to live it anymore.

WEARING HATS.

GAMBLING: Go back and reread the Las Vegas part.

ARGUING with neighbors over who owns what trees.

SPRAYING GRAFFITI: Increases visual acuity and a sense of community involvement.

BALLROOM DANCING: Keeps you in shape and lets you wear all kinds of spiffy outfits.

LEARNING SANSCRIT.

BECOMING A FASHION PLATE: To do so as a consumer, read *Women's Wear Daily*. To do so as a model, be beautiful and do not eat.

PAYING BILLS.

FIXING CLOCKS.

DARNING SOCKS.

WATCHING them unload trucks at the shopping center. A big favorite in Boise.

GETTING TAN.

If we still haven't found anything that does it for you, look on the bright side. You don't have to worry about killing time. You are already dead. Now the fun can really begin. Shame you will be too busy with your harp lessons and cloud patrol to enjoy it.

THREE:
Good Guys and Bad

7
House Calls

Like all great adventures, living features heroes and villains at every turn. No sooner do you survive one crisis than another pops up and forces you to call in the cavalry all over again. For the most part this scenario adds just enough spice to keep things interesting. "For the most part" does not, however, cover those nasty subplots which not only touch lives but frequently ruin them. Whether we care to admit it or not (and admitting has never been one of our longer suits), some of the things we do in our free time can wind up buying us more free time than we bargain for, can mess with the minds of those we love, can kill us.

Two ways to go at this point. The easy route pretends that tobacco addiction, alcoholism, drugs, stress, and their kin are someone else's problems. If that were the call, I could Mitch Miller us through a rousing sing-along of that great old reprobates' marching anthem "Cigareets and Whiskey and Wild, Wild Women" and make up a moderately amusing story of how Luther Terry got the idea for his eminently ignorable "Warning: The Surgeon General has determined that smoking is dangerous to your health" the night his wife turned the electric blanket up too high. The alternative is an uncharacteristically long, honest look in the mirror. Not as much fun but infinitely more likely to help us stay around awhile.

So now, with apologies to M. Python and his lunatic fringe, for something completely different: some straight talk concerning life's deadly serious side from those who know what they are talking about. Leaves me out. Over-the-counter aphorism and two-bit philosophy are okay treatment for the emotional acne we've bumped into so far, but malignancies demand expertise. That is why we shall spend the next few minutes here in the doctor's office. Correction: doctors' offices. In alphabetical order, our all-star HMO staff includes:

Alan Blum, M.D.
Editor, *New York State Journal of Medicine*
Founder of DOC (Doctors Ought to Care)

Willard A. Fry, M.D.
Chief, section of Thoracic Surgery
Evanston Hospital, Evanston, Illinois
Associate professor of clinical surgery, Northwestern University

Lee Gladstone, M.D.
Director, Chemical Dependency Unit,
  Martha Washington Hospital
Chairman, Impaired Physicians Committee,
  Illinois Medical Society
Past member, President's Advisory Committee

Robert L. Schmitz, M.D.
Chairman, Department of Surgery, Mercy Hospital/Medical Center
Past president, American Cancer Society of Illinois
President, Illinois Inter-Agency Council on Smoking and Disease

Sidney Schnoll, M.D.
Head of Chemical Dependence Program, Northwestern Memorial
  Hospital
Associate professor of psychology, behavioral sciences, and
  pharmacology, Northwestern University Medical School

Brenda Clorfene Solomon, M.D.
Faculty, Chicago Institute for Psychoanalysis
Clinical assistant professor of psychiatry, University of Chicago/
  Pritzker School of Medicine
Attending psychiatrist, Michael Reese Hospital

If that group cannot fix it, it probably cannot be fixed. Since more of us seem to have trouble kicking tobacco than most other rotten habits, smoking seems a logical point at which to start their meters ticking and find out. For purpose of clarification, I shall play the role of the Q in this hypothetical seminar. Q is not supposed to know many of the answers. Very solid casting.

Q: President Lyndon Johnson's physicians said he might have lived ten years longer had he not been such a heavy smoker. True or false?

Dr. Schmitz: Impossible to say without first-person knowledge of an individual's complete medical history, but if I were a betting man . . . Smoking's disastrous long-term effects are rather well documented, you know.

Dr. Blum: Just ask Amanda Blake, Kitty on "Gunsmoke," about the torture she went through with cancer of the larynx caused by smoking. Many women are luckier than she was. They just develop voices like foghorns and bad breath.

Dr. Fry: Senator Dirksen.

Dr. Blum: Dick Haymes, Nat ("King") Cole, Chet Huntley, Robert Taylor, Gary Cooper, Rosalind Russell—we could go through a catalogue of its victims, many of whom had appeared in cigarette ads. While dying from cigarette-induced lung cancer, Bill Talman, the DA on "Perry Mason," did a great thing by making commercials urging kids not to be "a loser," like he had been, by smoking cigarettes.

Q: Tyrone Power?

Dr. Blum: I think that was a heart attack. Induced by what, I don't recall, but yes I believe I read that cigarettes were involved at the time. Two of the best known, of course, were Humphrey Bogart and Edward R. Murrow.

Q: They all seem to have been old-timers. Is age a factor?

Dr. Fry: Yes, there is a definite time-dosage relationship. Don't see many high school kids coming down with lung cancer or emphysema.

Q: It's too bad that, when they show Bogart in *Casablanca* or whatever movie it is where he taps a cigarette on the back of his hand, they don't show a corresponding picture of his nine-hour operation for cancer of the larynx at age fifty-seven or whatever he went through.

Dr. Fry: Don't forget the Marlboro man.

Q: Who?

Dr. Blum: When last seen, he was wheezing his way off into the sunset.

Dr. Fry: Have you ever seen "A Death in the West"?

Q: No.

Dr. Fry: Do you know about it?

Q: No.

Dr. Fry: It was a British television documentary done several years ago that Philip Morris was able to have suppressed in this country until very recently, when a few public television stations got ahold of it. Uses a lot of the old Marlboro TV commercials along with interview footage of Montana and Wyoming cowboys who are, were, I suppose, dying of lung cancer. They and their doctors presented some rather stark contrasts to the pretty pictures. Dying of lung cancer isn't much fun.

Q: Oh, is it the one with the very long, beautiful shot of a cowboy riding toward the camera from a distant mountain range and eventually getting close enough for us to see that he is wearing an oxygen mask and has a tank strapped to his saddle?

Dr. Fry: That's the one. Really strong. The Lung Association has copies of it, which they are delighted to loan out for educational purposes.

Q: Bet the tobacco industry loves that.

Dr. Fry: Have you ever dealt with the Tobacco Institute? Believe me, they are very good at what they do. Very slick. Very smooth. Very persuasive.

Dr. Blum: The Marlboro cowboy is, of course, the real authority figure for our society. It's interesting that doctors and parents and teachers get blamed for everything, and the Marlboro fellow just sits up there astride that horse and he seems to change for the better. He gets younger and younger while all the rest of us get older and older. The cigarette manufacturers can change models every month, just like centerfolds, and naïve college kids will pose happily, not really understanding that they are leading kids into a world that won't be that romantic in the long run.

Q: Same go for his new counterpart, the girl in the satin pajamas?

Dr. Fry: Yeah, she is absolute dynamite.

Dr. Blum: Well, it's interesting . . . I'll tell you about that one. She represents a corporation which owns insurance companies and health maintenance organizations. The head of that company is the president of a major university medical center. Strange. Sick.

Q: Does he smoke?

Dr. Fry: Who knows? Not likely that you would ever get close enough to find out.

Dr. Blum: It is all pretty sick, but at least the satin girl probably has these marvelous yellow teeth now and they feel just like satin when you brush up against them. Grunge grows well on tobacco stains.

Q: Guess the kids don't see that side.

Dr. Blum: No way they could. The leading health educator of our time in our society is the cigarette industry. You think about it. When you go to a baseball game to watch those healthy ath-

letes, what's looming over them in almost every major-league stadium except for Wrigley Field? Of course, a cigarette billboard.
And when you open up a newspaper or *Time* magazine opposite
the medicine section or the health section, you will almost invariably find a cigarette ad. That is the whole point. There is a proverb
that says, "Truth is good, but juxtaposition is better." Remember
the ad "More doctors smoke Camels than any other cigarette?"
Ever see that thing? It led to the other one we used to always say as
kids, "Eight out of ten doctors prefer Camels. The other two prefer
women."

Q: No, you must be older than I am.

Dr. Blum: Funny.

Q: So that's what they do, put themselves next to acceptables?

Dr. Blum: Right, and that, too, is an important part of the
game. They are the leading financiers of the American printed
media today, which means that it and, in a sense, many of its
health-related news stories are associated opposite those pages with
cigarette ads. *Self* magazine is a good example. It advertises itself to
women as a health-oriented piece, and its leading advertiser category is cigarettes.

Q: Is that where the Kool Jazz Festival, Slims Tennis, and
whichever one of them underwrote the Vatican art exhibit come
into play?

Dr. Blum: On the money. It takes art to get a papal blessing
for what really amounts to pushing drugs. You've got to give them
credit for being able to somehow create the notion that this is just
another marvelous producer of fine products. Somehow they got
one of the spokespeople for the Vatican to say, "This is not Philip
Morris the cigarette company, this is Philip Morris International."
So I really think that it's a matter of people not understanding.
And if you go to its origins, the trouble really lies with the media.
We hear and read hundreds of stories about AIDS or legionnaire's
disease for every one we run into about something to do with ciga-

rettes or alcohol. But then, why should we hear more about those? They are very good advertisers, who it would not be nice to offend. I always visualize the relationship this way. Imagine one of these graphs that looks like the skyline of Chicago or some other big city. Way up at the top is the number of stories about saccharin or AIDS or legionnaire's disease. Way up at the top also are the number of deaths from cigarette-triggered lung cancer. Then way, way down at the bottom, at street level, is the number of real hard-hitting stories about cigarettes and the number of ad dollars from the gay bar or saccharin industries. You get a certain sense that what is covered the most threatens the least. I don't think any major industry is terribly threatened by a hard-hitting exposé of legionnaire's disease. Toxic shock and the Tylenol thing were obvious exceptions, and they were so much bigger than life there probably would not have been any realistic way to bury them.

Q: I read somewhere that it is the American Medical Association's resolution to have a smoke-free society by the year 2000. Is that, pardon the expression, a pipe dream?

Dr. Blum: I hope this means the AMA is getting serious about efforts to curtail smoking. In my experience, the product with the longest shelf life in the United States is an American Medical Association resolution. The AMA has been passing them for years but has yet to really back them up with any substantive financial or lobbying commitment. It doesn't go into Congress with anything approaching the strength it brings to bear against health insurance bills or whatever. I, for one, would be much more proud of the AMA if it would do something more than send out a one-page statement saying, "We support antismoking legislation."

Q: Like the man said, "You don't understand politics."

Dr. Fry: Well, I do not personally think that anyone could come in right now and arbitrarily cut off tobacco support. It wouldn't be fair. I think it should be phased out gradually. There are people who have had their livelihood based in the industry for centuries. You can't go take some farmer up along the Connecticut River valley or down in Virginia and all of a sudden cut the crops out from under him without offering . . . I would love to see them have a governmentally sponsored alternative schooling program. Send them back to ag school. Send some of the ag department guys out to really work with them, that sort of thing.

Dr. Blum: Voters probably would not stand for anything precipitous anyway.

Q: They just did in San Francisco, didn't they?

Dr. Fry: Sort of. And Minneapolis and a couple of other places, but on the whole, no. Not yet. Besides, this has been a very essential part of American commerce since the seventeenth century. I was reading an autobiography of Thomas Jefferson a few years ago, and he was always in debt and hoping that increased tobacco sales to the British would enable him to retire his outstanding loans.

Q: But the suppression of the devastating effects of this for so long is really a thing to deal with, isn't it?

Dr. Schmitz: Of course, but not only the long-term horrors everyone has heard about. I think we should spend a minute on smoking's less spectacular immediate effects. They are easy for you to check for yourself if you have ever smoked. Have you?

Q: Yes, but I was lucky. I quit.

Dr. Fry: Me too. But you know as well as I do that luck had nothing to do with it. To quit, you have to want to quit and do it. Tough but not impossible. That is important.

Dr. Schmitz: If a smoker takes his or her pulse, there will be an increase in its rate very quickly after you begin to inhale. That, of course, raises your blood pressure by constricting your blood vessels. The constriction leaves less space for blood, and the pressure goes up. But in addition, that means your skin gets cold, and people that have, for instance, trouble with blood vessels in their legs due to restricted blood supply are much worse off with smoking. In fact, in extreme cases it can actually lead to gangrene of the feet.

Q: You're kidding. No, you aren't, are you?

Dr. Schmitz: The bronchial tubes in your lungs also constrict, which makes it more difficult to breathe.

Q: Emphysema?

Dr. Fry: Long before emphysema. That is generally one of the time-dosed grand prizes for playing cigarette bingo.

Dr. Schmitz: We're still at the beginner's level. Your senses are dulled. I guess everyone knows that taste and smell and touch are dulled almost immediately by smoking. And of course, smoking exaggerates asthma in some people. It irritates and eventually causes cancers in the gastrointestinal tract, particularly in the swallowing tube, the esophagus. It affects the pancreas, which is the sweetbread, and it affects the kidney and the bladder. And the brain—it can lead to strokes. We know definitively that in pregnancy the babies are smaller and born earlier, which puts them at much higher risk. So mothers who smoke are doing that. And then, finally, the oral cavity is affected very dramatically.

Q: I saw a United Press release contending that smoke is the biggest nemesis of people with gum problems. Quoting the American Dental Association, it said, "Gum disease, principal cause of tooth loss in adults, has been clearly associated with smoking." The stuff gets you at every turn.

Dr. Blum: Don't forget the wonderfully cosmetic effect is has on your teeth, breath, and face. Those crows'-feet are much more common on smokers. It has a general aging effect on skin because it is a little like putting a blow dryer to your face, from the inside out. It literally sucks moisture from vessels, makes them brittle by depriving them of oxygen.

Q: Fascinating. Frightening but fascinating. Does anyone really know what all is in cigarette smoke?

Dr. Blum: Maybe the companies who make them.

Q: Maybe?

Dr. Blum: Certainly no one else does. The boys in the back room say they cannot reveal their secrets for fear of having competitors duplicate best-selling special blends and flavors. What little we know comes from independent chemical analysis. Things like propylene glycol.

Q: Is that one of the secret flavoring agents?

Dr. Blum: One of its uses is as an automotive brake solvent. The cigarette companies use it as a moisturizing agent in tobacco.

Dr. Fry: There are over a thousand phantom goodies in there.

Dr. Blum: I have seen estimates ranging as high as fifteen hundred. One of my favorite is deer tongue. It contains an anticoagulant that could cause many people to suffer serious clotting disorders. And as I said, they're not even revealing any of this. It all had to be found out by chemical analysis. So when you hear that, you wonder why it is that the very consumers of the product have come to the aid of the industry, so to speak, by saying, "Oh, no, that's my right, and this is my product." You would think that they themselves would be the most angry, like the Republicans would have been when Nixon was found to have done all the things with Watergate. But instead, you know, the psychology somehow will be to stick with them until the end.

Q: Maybe the warning should read, "incidentally these things will kill you!"

Dr. Blum: That's good. I think basically anytime people hear the real story of that industry, if it can ever get out, that will be hazardous to their sensibilities.

Q: That will never get out, will it?

Dr. Blum: Yes, I think so. I think we are already getting the word out slowly. It is just a matter of proportion. I think that the industry is really less blameworthy than some of the major publishing companies. I really believe that if the publishing industry, which fifteen years ago was the one that was clamoring most for the expulsion of cigarette ads from radio and TV, were to take stock of itself and of what we know by saying, "Yes, it's legal, but it's wrong, and we shall therefore no longer accept its ads," we would all be a lot better off. There are a few magazines, such as the *New Yorker*, which do not accept them. But in general terms, most publishers seem more concerned with hazards to their wealth than to their health. Not terribly civic-minded, I'm afraid.

Q: Gets us back to some of the payoffs. What was that bingo number you mentioned earlier?

Dr. Fry: The big three—heart attacks, lung cancer, and emphysema. Play long enough, and you are almost certain to have an inside shot at one or more of them. Other diseases are worth extra points when scoring the game. Urinary bladder cancer is becoming a popular add-on. I frankly do not believe that people are aware of all of the possibilities—no, probabilities—involved in smoking. There was some suggestion of danger back in the forties and fifties, but the hard evidence didn't come out until ten or twenty years ago.

Q: The surgeon general's report?

Dr. Fry: And the Framingham study. Framingham is a suburb outside of Boston. Twenty or twenty-five years ago a huge governmental grant was put out through the Harvard School of Public Health to study cardiovascular risk factors. They got thousands of people registered. Used cardiograms, questionnaires, serial measurements of cholesterol levels, blood pressure, presence or absence of diabetes, and all these things and then followed all the cardiovascular risk factors for, I'm sure, it is over twenty years now. And the one thing that correlates the most with death from first heart attack is not diabetes. It is not cholesterol count. It is not fat in the diet. It is not family history or hypertension. It is whether or not you are a smoker.

Q: Is that right?

Dr. Fry: Absolutely phenomenal.

Q: How does it happen? What exactly is the process of deterioration physically? Are the lungs affected first? This constant three- or four-pack-a-day habit—what happens?

Dr. Fry: Let's pick the lungs because they are almost easier to deal with. Lung cancer is now the number one cancer killer in American men and the number two cancer killer in American women.

Q: Women? I didn't realize they had anywhere near as much trouble with it as men.

Dr. Blum: There are places where female lung cancers have actually surpassed male rates. The best records are kept in Connecticut by the health commissioner, a Dr. Doug Lloyd. He has been a marvelous help in this area and has identified definite patterns of dramatic increase in female lung cancers.

Dr. Fry: And if their smoking tendencies continue, by the end of the 1980s or sooner it'll be the number one cancer killer in American women. Breast cancers will still be more common, but their cure rate is reasonable, whereas it stinks in lung cancer. So that's sort of what we're dealing with. There will be something like one hundred thirty thousand new cases in America this year. At the end of five years only ten percent of all comers are alive to tell about it.

Dr. Schmitz: You know, we thought for a while that there was a difference between the sexes when it came to their susceptibility. Not so. It takes ten to fifteen, even twenty years for changes from the carcinogens, not only in tobacco but all through life. Anything we eat or inhale takes a long time to take effect. Now that women have been smoking in large numbers long enough, their incidence of cancer of the lung is almost going in an epidemic proportion upward. Really it's something. It's so evident that I don't see how it can be overlooked. So they are not safe either. What's worse, smoking does not only produce cancer in the lungs. Emphysema is a horrible disease which is almost always due to smoking, and it cannot be corrected.

Q: I would be willing to wager that nine out of ten people don't know what emphysema even is.

Dr. Blum: Well, it's very hard. I don't think that you or I really know what any disease is all about until we get it. Then we become very angry and agitated and wonder why it couldn't have happened to someone else instead. Believe me, emphysema is the worst thing you can have. Lung cancer is almost a blessing compared to it. You are dying very slowly, and you can feel it happening. You know how it feels when you go underwater, and you stay there for perhaps a bit too long, and when you come up, you are gasping desperately for breath? Well, that is precisely what it is like to live with emphysema all the time.

Q: And it is absolutely irreversible?

Dr. Blum: Yes. Have you ever popped those little bubbles on sheets of plastic insulating paper? That's what emphysema is like. The heat from the smoke and the other irritants just pop those sacs in the lungs. Just like popcorn.

Q: Is there any such thing as a safe amount of smoking one can do?

Dr. Fry: That is frequently asked, but it is an awfully hard question to answer because you would really have to do a controlled clinical trial on that to come close to accurate information. You know, you would have to collect a large number of volunteers and say, "All right now, you guys, you smoke ten cigarettes a day, and we'll follow you around for twenty-five years and see what happens." I would be hard pressed to say that a little old lady who smoked one cigarette a day would axiomatically be killing herself, but it just doesn't work that way. People who smoke, usually smoke a lot: a pack or more a day.

Dr. Schmitz: The damage that is done is in direct proportion to the amount of tobacco that is used and, usually, the period of time over which it is used. But nevertheless, there isn't any right amount to be safe. Even one a day could be very harmful to people who are susceptible to tobacco, so we shouldn't even think about that.

Dr. Blum: The safe amount of smoke is no smoke. Period!

Dr. Schmitz: The same thing applies to the special filters the industry is so fond of promoting. Theoretically, if you filter out some of the tar and smoke, you will be better off. However, if the filter is at all effective, the tobacco doesn't taste right to the users, so they do not like those cigarettes. They tend to keep going back to the stronger ones. The other thing about filters is: They often put even more additives into the tobacco. We suspect that some of these additives haven't been checked out very thoroughly as yet. They could be a very bad thing.

Dr. Fry: The use of filtered cigarettes is increasing. Cigarette-related illness is not decreasing. I rest my case.

Q: Hugh Hefner, Columbo, and the rest of the pipe and cigar puffers who don't inhale seem to consider themselves perfectly safe. Are they?

Dr. Blum: Every bit as safe as a leopard trainer compared to a lion tamer. It may work differently from one medium to another, but smoke is smoke.

Dr. Schmitz: Definitely not. Pipes and cigars simply affect different areas than cigarettes. They don't get down into the lungs as much, but they usually hit the mouth, voice box, and swallowing tube even more traumatically. Cancer of the larynx, the voice box, is very high in cigar and pipe smokers. Even chewing tobacco can produce cancer of the mouth. No, there is no safe form of tobacco.

Dr. Fry: The data is not as absolutely convincing as for cigarettes but certainly clear enough for my money. The incidence of oral cancer seems to be up for pipe and cigar smokers over nonsmokers. Perhaps the most dangerous thing about cigars is that people who are trying to quit cigarettes often use them as substitutes and wind up inhaling them. Real trouble. I know. Did it myself for a while. Whew!

Q: Can we go back to the pregnant woman issue again?

Dr. Fry: Pregnant women who smoke tend to have more premature babies than nonsmokers, and premies tend to have many more problems than full-term babies. The other thing, not too far removed from the subject, that is interesting is that there seems to be a connection of some kind evolving between cigarette smoking and birth control pills. It has not yet been totally defined, but it appears to be a ticking time bomb. Historically women in their childbearing years have not had cardiovascular difficulties. In recent years there has been a very significant increase in the number of young women who both smoke and take the pill having heart attacks and strokes. Potentially very bad news.

Q: What's the real story about the threat to nonsmokers who live with or work around smokers? Is the San Francisco law merely for comfort, or does safety enter the picture?

Dr. Fry: Secondhand smoking definitely irritates certain diseases, such as asthma. There was a large Japanese study published in the British *Journal of Medicine* a couple of years ago which indicated the effects spread much further. It reported a definitely higher incidence of lung cancer among nonsmokers whose spouses smoked. Intriguing phenomenon. A doctor in Long Beach has been able to show that cardiac irregularities and the severity of angina are increased in people who are exposed to secondhand smoke. I don't think it is harmless by any stretch of the imagination. I'm not sure it is as dangerous as some of the real antismoking health nuts believe, but there is certainly nothing harmless about it.

Dr. Blum: If I spit on you, it doesn't mean you are going to get tuberculosis, but the fact is it is pretty vulgar. At the very least it is a terrifically selfish act. If you feel yourself about to break wind in someone's office, the odds are that you will either try to beat a hasty retreat or apologize embarrassedly. As far as I'm concerned, it is the same thing with cigarettes. Yet most people don't think twice about lighting up. Again advertising is primarily at fault. It always positions smoking in situations which would seem least amenable to it. It encourages people to smoke at the dinner table—during appetizers, no less. Now that, you must admit, is foul.

Dr. Schmitz: It is dangerous. Definitely. Evidence is coming in. For a long time that was the argument. Smokers said it was a personal matter, that if they wanted to gamble with their health, it was their business and prerogative to do so. Two recent studies, from Creighton and the University of California at San Diego, have shown that passive smoking triggers a higher incidence of lung and heart problems. No question. I hope the San Francisco and Minneapolis experiments are successful enough to push things much further very quickly.

Dr. Fry: Dream on. We tried to have similar laws passed in Chicago a couple of years ago, and the tobacco industry came on like a ton of bricks. As I said earlier, they are very good at what they do. Of course, there appears to be more to it than merely inhaling others' smoke residue. Smoking-related disorders are much more common in heavily industrialized areas than their rural equivalents, so there is probably something to be said for overall environment's impact. To be honest, nobody really has the answers yet. Why does one guy get lung cancer, and another three-pack-a-day man not? Why is lung cancer sky-high among uranium workers and asbestos workers who smoke? The radon gas in uranium mines is probably synergistic with cigarettes in the production of cancer, but frankly we just don't know. That is why research is so crucially important.

Q: Are we ever going to reach the smoke-free society goal?

Dr. Fry: In this country, perhaps. Worldwide? I seriously doubt that. Do you realize that we are, at this very minute, exporting tobacco to third world countries as part of our Food for Peace program?

Dr. Blum: With that kind of patriotic trade policy going for us, about the only way we are likely to escape the weed is if someone does an AIDS public relations number in the tobacco area. Someone prints a few headlines reading EIGHTEEN CASES OF LEPROSY REPORTED AT R. J. REYNOLDS, and maybe, just maybe, we would see some action.

Q: Have a hot-button medical crisis handy?

Dr. Blum: Yes, as a matter of fact, I do. Methicillin. Methicillin resistance *Staphylococcus aureus*, to be exact. That's a crazy name for a hospital infection that was all the rage in Australia awhile back. People going in for various surgical procedures were dying or coming down with very serious infections. I think it will be our next big epidemic sensation in this country. Definitely hot copy.

Q: How will we know it, by its initials?

Dr. Blum: MRSA. Count on it.

Q: Nice to have something to look forward to. So, if the industry isn't going to go away in one last glorious puff of smoke, people are probably going to have to quit on their own. Can they? You hear it all the time: "Oh, I'm not addicted to smoking. I could quit if I wanted to. It's just a habit." True or false?

Dr. Solomon: Well, something that is habitual like cigarette smoking has multiple levels of meaning. Even though someone knows better intellectually, there is a disparity between what one knows intellectually and what one is able to do emotionally. Cigarette smoking has some actual addictive properties, physically addictive properties, but they are not as powerful as its emotionally addicting behavior, which users grow to feel they need to soothe pressures or quiet anxieties or the like.

Dr. Schmitz: False. For at least a quarter of smokers there is an addiction at work here. They are dependent upon a drug, and the drug is nicotine. It affects the ganglion cells in the nervous system and has a kind of relaxing effect, a calming effect, and that is what they like about smoking. But it is the same thing, then, that leads to the increased pulse rate and blood pressure and so forth. So those people will get withdrawal symptoms, just like a drug addict will, and it is definitely pretty rough for them to stop. On the brighter side, even they can be helped, and the other seventy-five percent can really stop "cold turkey" if they learn to do something else with their hands, with their mouths, with all the little things, the reflex habits they've built up around their smoking habit. You know, tapping it on the back of the hand and putting it in the mouth, rolling it around. If you work with them and teach them to do substitute things and to divert themselves when those urges come on, they can usually quit rather quickly.

Q: Humphrey Bogart at work again. Would it do any good if smokers could peek over the surgeon's shoulder and see exactly what infected lungs look like?

Dr. Fry: Scare tactics don't seem to work. Probably never will. I think you have to appeal to good sense and let people know that if they really want to quit, they can pull it off. I had to stop three or four or five times before I stayed stopped. The biggest challenge we all have is to stop making it look so damned attractive for young people.

Q: The Marlboro man?

Dr. Fry: That and "You've come a long way, baby," and the rest of the propaganda. I remember, when I started, I was a junior in high school, and I used to get sick. I'd get nauseated and sometimes throw up. But by the time I got to college, I was able to smoke like a real man. I honestly believe making it unattractive and undesirable is the key. America and the world in general are on sort of a health kick. I think particularly for girls in athletic performance and stuff like that, you are seeing, percentage-wise, fewer young people smoke now than were doing so five or ten years ago.

Dr. Schmitz: There are many, many approaches we do not have time to go into in detail at the moment, but I think you put your finger on the big thing: motivation. It does not matter how addictive or how difficult it is for anyone, when the motivation to quit is strong enough, they will have no trouble. Often you will see someone really, honestly try, unsuccessfully, to shake the habit. Then someone very close to them, a wife or parent, gets lung cancer. They put two and two together, and they stop overnight. Just like that! The others need to have group therapy, working together with others in the same boat through organization, such as the "I Quit!" clinics. It is very important, just as it is in drinking, that they be taught how to use substitutes for all of the little reflex actions they have developed. There is a nicotine gum which I consider effective and reasonably safe as a transitional crutch. Then low-calorie things like carrots and celery so they won't buy themselves another problem for their trouble. The important thing is: With encouragement, at least one out of three smokers who try, sincerely try will make it almost immediately, and, of the rest, another one or two will make it eventually. With the success of AA for those with alcohol problems, I think smokers anonymous groups deserve much more support.

Dr. Blum: You could always do it the way Jerry Lewis and Buddy Rich did recently. Both had emergency bypass operations and say it did wonders for their resolve when it came to lighting up.

Dr. Schmitz: Do you realize that is now the single most common operation being performed on men, more frequent even than appendectomies and gallbladder cuts, and that it could be virtually eliminated without cigarettes on the market? That brings in the whole new dimension of cost. These things are milking their users dry!

Dr. Blum: Well, maybe something good comes of it all. I think Jerry Lewis is doing a very good thing now by sheepishly, belatedly apologizing for the poor role modeling he has been doing all these years. I suppose what people do in their private lives ought to remain their own call, but when they flaunt a stupid life-style, like Roger Moore getting out of his limo with a fag, that's sick. I certainly applaud those in public view, Prince Charles, Lady Di, Larry Hagman, and the rest of them, who are not afraid to stand up for the nonsmokers movement.

Q: Hear, hear. That is absolutely the first argument in favor of either royalty or "Dallas" I have ever heard. Thanks. Makes me feel better about the world already. Speaking of feeling better, can they? Smokers, I mean. Once they do kick it, can the effects be reversed?

Dr. Schmitz: That is the good news. Now there are a couple of exceptions. Emphysema will not change, you will not get back your breathing capacity once it is lost, but at least it will not progress. And the other, of course, is a cancer which has already locked onto a vital organ. Too late. But under all other circumstances, no matter how long you have smoked, if you stop, you win. For instance, the little hairs in the lungs that keep clearing out the debris that gets down there—they are called cilia—will come back to life. They will once again begin to bring up the secretions. The coughing will let up. Your capacity to breathe will be improved, and all the other changes will get better so you can always say, yes, no matter how long you have smoked, if you stop, you will definitely be better off. If you have not yet had permanent damage, you will improve.

Dr. Fry: As he said, the literal answer is no. If someone has contracted certain disorders, they will do better because the irritation will be gone, but destroyed lung tissue simply cannot be regenerated. What you are born with is all you get. That is why these chronic airway diseases are so insidious. They sort of sneak up, and their victims usually do not realize how much trouble they are in until it is almost too late. Then they have to undergo big operations or painful therapy or whatever. Now the chronic bronchitis bit, for some reason, these guys tend to get a lot of irritation and then tend to get mucus and phlegm. They are called blue bloaters. Cough up a lot of gunk. See a lot of that sort of thing in England and in those industrial towns where there is heavy cigarette smoking. As far as the cardiovascular system, that seems to be less with the tar stuff and more with the nicotine and carbon monoxide. It all seems to have some kind of vasospastic component to it and seems to keep the blood vessels in spasms state, which promotes blockage and the buildup of, you know, fatty deposits. Messy business to get rid of even once the person involved gets uninvolved. Messy but not impossible for most.

Q: Hey, where does marijuana fit into all this? Do its users face the same grief?

Dr. Schmitz: We really don't know much about the carcinogens in marijuana. It may be no more harmful in some ways than smoking a lettuce leaf. That was tried, you know. Tasted absolutely terrible. Shame because it would not have had the tars in it that tobacco does.

Q: So why didn't they stick a few thousand of those fancy secret flavoring agents and brake fluids in it?

Dr. Schmitz: You would have to ask them. Already had a bunch of tobacco planted, I guess. In any event, there simply hasn't been much research into the physical dangers of marijuana. The ones we know about are more in the genetic process, the chromosomes, so that the offspring of its users can be born defective. Then, also, of course, it clouds judgment much like alcohol does, and it leads to stronger and stronger addicting drugs so frequently. That is why I would be against it.

Dr. Fry: The data are really skimpy. To start out with, as I said earlier, it is very hard to find a regular cigarette smoker who does less than a pack a day. I'm not sophisticated, personally, in the marijuana practice, but I would think that somebody who is going to have twenty hits of pot a day is going to be pretty well stoned most of the time, and the kind of time-dose relationship necessary for most of cigarettes' nastier results to take hold would, I presume, be darned near impossible to re-create with marijuana. I'm not saying it is any great thing, just that it is a different kind of problem.

Dr. Blum: The one saving grace of marijuana is you physically just cannot consume that much of it. If you could, the effects would be even worse because it is actually a much more concentrated, much more potent material than tobacco. Definitely heavier in tars and resins. Ever stop to think about that? Smoking puts tar into your body. No euphemism—literally tar. The real black, gooey gunk they use on roofs and roads. Tar is poison, period—a combination of about four thousand different chemicals, many of which are known to cause cancers. And it sticks to your body the same way it sticks to roadbeds. It cannot be expelled. Just sticks to your lungs and makes it tougher and tougher for them to do their job until, if you are lucky, you die of a heart attack. If you are unlucky, you get emphysema or lung cancer, both of which are pure torture.

Q: Great point, the one about all these things having been around for years. The beautiful people probably would be crushed to learn they are not at the cutting edge of avant hip. Cole Porter wrote a hit song in the thirties. One of its lyric lines was "Some get their kicks from cocaine . . ." Guess the blizzard of the eighties isn't quite as with it as its press clippings crack it up to be.

Dr. Schnoll: Cocaine, coke, as I guess most people know it today, has been around forever. It was very heavily used around the turn of the century. Soft drinks like Coca-Cola actually contained cocaine back then. There were cocaine wines, cocaine medicines, cocaine candles available almost everywhere. With the passage of the Pure Food and Drug Act, cocaine was taken out of many of these substances, but there is obviously still a rather general use of it by many people. Its recent resurgence probably has a lot to do with our times, with the pervasive narcissism that exists in our society.

Q: Ground zero question: What are we talking about? What exactly is coke, and why do people use it?

Dr. Schnoll: A drug, both a central nervous system stimulant and a local anesthetic. People take it primarily for its stimulating properties. When people take it, they tend to feel more alert, feel as though they have increased energy; [it] makes them feel like they are capable of doing more, better. They get a feeling of increased confidence and control. So someone who is trying to follow a hard day's work with a hard night's socializing frequently feels he or she needs something like coke to provide a boost. Cocaine fills the bill. In addition, its high cost makes it very glamorous, very appealing to some individuals' personal narcissism. It's a status symbol.

Q: None of that sounds as damning as I had expected it to. Are you saying we're all being too uptight about its apparent popularity?

Dr. Schnoll: No. Cocaine is an interesting drug in that, with small amounts there are some studies which indicate that people actually do perform somewhat better. But as the dose increases, the pattern is reversed, and performance impaired. The big problem arises because people frequently do not know how much coke they are buying on the street or what the quality of it is. As a result, they can go from the slight improvement stage into functional impairment very quickly.

Q: Does a user require increasing amounts to achieve the same effect over time? Is there a body tolerance or immunity level?

Dr. Schnoll: Well, people do become somewhat tolerant to its effects and take increasing dosages. The tolerance level doesn't seem to develop as rapidly as with some other drugs, but yes, doses do tend to increase over time.

Q: Is there a physical dependency?

Dr. Schnoll: The classic literature says no. However, as we're seeing more and more people using cocaine in increasing amounts, I think clinically we are also beginning to see a withdrawal syndrome that is characteristic and would mean there is some physical dependency involved.

Q: Is there any frequency that is safe or at least tolerable?

Dr. Schnoll: Difficult to say. On the basis of present data, a recreational user, someone who does small amounts once or twice a month doesn't seem to wind up with any major problems. But we do not have enough documentation to give a precise level at which it begins to be trouble. Turning that around, nor do we know when it is little enough not to be trouble.

Q: Is coke the most commonly used drug at the moment or simply the most publicized?

Dr. Schnoll: Indications are that over twenty million Americans have now tried it, and there are probably several million more using it on a fairly regular basis. It is definitely not solely a celebrity situation.

Q: Are coke and alcohol or marijuana "highs" the same?

Dr. Schnoll: Quite, quite different. Marijuana, alcohol are sedative drugs. They tend to depress the nervous system. They tend to make people more relaxed, whereas cocaine is a stimulant. It heightens the central nervous system so a person becomes more active, sometimes almost hyper.

Q: Recent headlines concerning Richard Pryor, John Belushi, assorted pro athletes, and the like have made *free basing* part of the common vernacular. Usage is one thing. Understanding is quite another. What is it?

Dr. Schnoll: Free basing is a technique that takes coke as it is normally prepared, as an acid salt, and converts it into a nonsalt state that volatizes at a lower temperature. Since it then becomes a gas at a lower temperature, it can be smoked, inhaled. Dangerous. There is some recent evidence from our own labs here at Northwestern and from some other places that the technique tends to get people more intensely involved with the drug much more rapidly. People tend to deteriorate very rapidly once they start free basing. We even have some very recent data which indicates that it can cause some severe changes to the lungs which may not be reversible.

Q: The lungs seem to be the big losers with all of this junk. I may have asked this earlier, but have you been able to observe whether coke users, by and large, can get off the stuff?

Dr. Schnoll: It's very hard to have any real numbers on that. I think probably cocaine is like many other drugs in that regard. There are people who can use it recreationally and not get into problems. But there are then people who go on and use increasing amounts and get into real trouble. I do not believe anyone knows exactly what proportion of the total number of triers ever become severely impaired.

Q: As far as danger is concerned, where does it fit in on the rating system with heroin and other known, frequently used drugs?

Dr. Schnoll: Again, we need more time to see what happens to heavy users. We've had experience with heavy users of many other drugs, but the cocaine phenomenon, in terms of heavy use, is somewhat more recent. Can't really put it on that spectrum yet.

Q: If it stimulates, instead of sedates, is there any danger for a coke user driving a car?

Dr. Schnoll: As research volunteers take in increasing amounts under laboratory conditions, their coordination definitely becomes impaired. So that could certainly affect driving. But whereas with alcohol we have specific, defined levels of intoxication, I don't know of anybody who has determined such levels in terms of cocaine.

Dr. Blum: We are just beginning to look at that kind of thing. There really isn't any simple test for substances like marijuana or cocaine. You have to measure its level in the blood. Without a breath test or its equivalent, I can be totally stoned, and a policeman, if he doesn't know what questions to ask or what to look for, will let me go even if I have been weaving all over the road.

He has no proof of inebriation. This is a problem. In some states—California is one of them—estimates are that three out of five people stopped for apparent drunken driving are actually on coke or marijuana or the like. One simple thing that could help detect them would be to ask a suspect to "Tell me when thirty seconds are up." Users tend to lose a sense of time, so they will normally answer after about five seconds. It isn't being done much yet, but it should.

Q: Are there any warning signs or indicators that would warn a user that he or she is getting in too deep?

Dr. Schnoll: Anybody who thinks he might be using too much is probably using too much. If it even crosses the mind that you are using the drug too much, you probably are.

Q: Will legalizing help?

Dr. Schnoll: Legalizing would probably do a couple of things. It would probably mean that more people would try it. So it would increase the number of users. It would bring the price down significantly. That would also tend to increase the number of users. There's two, I think, on the negative side. On the positive, it would reduce the number of impurities that we now find in samples of cocaine. Many samples contain other drugs which can be quite deleterious. We have found samples that contain things like PCP in them. We certainly know that's not a drug that most people want to take. It would clean up that problem, but there would be increased users. I'm not sure that it would solve anything particularly by legalizing it.

Q: Let's turn to something they have already legalized, relegalized, I suppose, to be accurate. Booze. Stories regarding the imbibing habits of W. C. Fields and John Barrymore and several latter-day tipsters are legendary. They say Errol Flynn, for example, put away a quart of vodka or gin every day for the last twenty years of his life. What in heaven's name does that sort of thing do to the human body?

Dr. Gladstone: Well, one must know and understand what happens to alcohol. Whatever you drink—wine, whiskey, or beer—they all contain certain, albeit varying, amounts of alcohol. That alcohol metabolizes in the human body at a rate of about an ounce every hour to hour and a half. It does not take a mathematician or blood chemist to work out the equation. More ounces in the body than hours in the day means Errol Flynn had to have been drunk all of the time. That heavy a drinker makes an adaptation to it. He adjusts himself and learns how to manage himself with that much alcohol in there so that he has a behavior that is acceptable to most people. They may not like him, but he will not usually be rejected by everyone immediately. Over the years, of course, the brain is involved, and there is a gradual deterioration in its capacity to relate to and process information. As a result, the drinker's ability to relate to others in a warm, compassionate, consistent way diminishes. Eventually his total network, his social network begins to change. Physically the heart enlarges and the muscle gets weaker. The liver becomes damaged. Although the body also adapts itself to these changes, a man whose body is broken down obviously is not likely to live as long as someone who is healthy. There are exceptions who can get by with steady alcohol consumption over a prolonged period, but they are, by definition, exceptions.

Q: The norm is debilitation, emotional and physical self-destruction?

Dr. Gladstone: Yes. Alcohol not only damages the body but is reflected in relationships with other people as well. The heavy drinker often loses his family. He is divorced many, many times. His children are alienated from him. He is difficult to work with. No one really wants to be involved with that kind of person. If these people have unique qualities, as Errol Flynn did as an actor, these qualities also deteriorate. In his case the number of movies he would have made in later life and the quality of roles offered to him no doubt gradually deteriorated over a time until he was probably isolated even from his own profession.

Q: The classic skid. When do you suppose he was too far gone to turn back? Is there any way for a person to tell when he is leaving the ranks of the moderate or heavy drinkers' world and becoming too dependent upon alcohol? Any signs there for him to see?

Dr. Gladstone: Nothing precise, but, yes, there are some general warning signs to look out for. Suddenly he finds that he takes the extra, has another drink with the boys, or without them, and discovers he cannot stop when he wants to. He then enters into the common term of "denial." He says, "Well, I'm not really drinking that much." He moves into the position where he simply cannot stop. His work performance goes down. His family begins to complain. His good friends say to him, "Hey, Joe, you're drinking too much." And he says, "No. I'm really not. I can handle it. I'm okay. Just got a raise, that's all." But the raise somehow or other isn't there the next time. And so he moves into such a degree of dependence that he really can't stop, and then he is hooked because in the morning he has a little shake or he is very nervous. He becomes irritable and edgy. There is a whole progression of these kind of symptoms.

Q: Let's try this another way. If a man has a couple of martinis for lunch and a glass of wine, then goes home and has cocktails before dinner, another glass or two of wine, brandy after dinner— is that too much?

Dr. Gladstone: I think that would be too much. When you say a two-martini lunch with a glass of wine, that is approximately equal to five shots of whiskey before the poor guy even gets home. It would take the body anywhere from five to seven hours to metabolize that much alcohol. By *metabolize,* I mean the work that the liver has to do to either make the alcohol usable to the rest of the body or to break it down so it can be excreted. As I indicated, it can only do a small part in any one moment. As the alcohol is absorbed from the intestine, the liver begins to work on the alcohol, but the rest of it floats freely through your body: going through your arteries and veins; going to the heart, the brain, the bones, even the sex organs. It is going through the entire body and damaging all of those cells in the process. Some cells, particularly those in the brain, are more susceptible than others. So I would say that is an excessive amount of drinking. If someone has a two-martini lunch with wine and cocktails before dinner and another glass of wine or two and maybe a snifter of brandy afterwards as a matter of routine, I'm afraid I would have to classify that person as an alcoholic.

Q: What about our friend who had too much weekend and vows to himself "Never again!" and means it . . . until the next weekend?

Dr. Solomon: There is something different that happens on the weekend, without the controls and structure of the work environment, that makes your friend have to resort to an added way to medicate himself—that's what he is trying to do, you know—against an angry and bitter wife, needy children, leaky pipes, a mother-in-law, or whatever. People who resort to these extreme behaviors do so because they cannot regulate their anxieties, their anger, their distress.

Q: Is there any absolutely safe amount for a person to ingest regularly?

Dr. Gladstone: There is not one safe amount. It depends upon the internal controls of the individual involved. Some people can sit down and have a couple of drinks every evening and do quite well with it. Others can sit down and have two drinks for an evening for this year or next year, and maybe in the third or fourth year they're up to three, and maybe they'll pick up one at noon. It's not a predictable thing. However, I would say if one has a couple of drinks a day—no more, no less—I don't think it would be that harmful. I wouldn't drink that much because even small amounts of alcohol can cause damage in the susceptible individual, and you simply cannot predict who that susceptible individual is going to be until it is perhaps too late.

Dr. Schmitz: Gets us back to some of the other problems as well. If a person drinks heavily and smokes at the same time, that's a very serious matter for cancer of the lung and all the rest of what we discussed earlier.

Q: What about the person who drinks quite heavily most of the time but occasionally tries to dry out by going into periods of abstinence, six or seven weeks every year—something like that?

Dr. Gladstone: He's fooling himself. Even though he takes six or seven weeks a year off, there are fifty-two of them in a year, and the rest of the time the damage continues. The cells continue to swell and die. Little scars form throughout the body: scars in the brain, scars in the liver, scars in the bone. Six weeks of abstinence? He's really deceiving himself.

Q: What about the advice for the man who erroneously describes himself as a social or just a moderate drinker who really isn't? How can he arrest the deception?

Dr. Solomon: The first step is acknowledging the nature of the problem, and that's real, real hard to do. If, however, someone can acknowledge that they have a problem that they have not been able to solve themselves, they are halfway home. The other step, of course, is deciding where to turn. Certainly with drinking you can never go wrong with Alcoholics Anonymous and similar treatment programs. But the first step is definitely acknowledging the problem.

Q: Can an alcoholic—what exactly is that, by the way?—recover, then convert back to moderate drinking?

Dr. Blum: I have some trouble with terms that stigmatize. The definition that I use is somebody who drinks more than his doctor. When I ask a patient how much he or she drinks, I usually take the answer and double it automatically. If that adds up to more than my own level of impropriety, it spells trouble.

Dr. Gladstone: I'm sure there are moderate drinkers out there, but I don't know any. All the people I deal with have been serious drinkers and people that are addicted. But the question I would ask: Why would someone who has been through the hell of reforming from alcoholism ever want to risk it again? What kind of chances do you want to take? What kind of risk? If you are an alcoholic, you are an alcoholic, and absolute abstinence is the goal. No, more than the goal—the necessity.

Q: Are there any childhood personality traits or warning signs? Any genetic vulnerability to alcohol?

Dr. Gladstone: There are some interesting things going on in that area. A Dr. Goodwin, who is the head of psychiatry at the University of Kansas, has looked at twin studies, identical twins of parents who were alcoholic. In Denmark, for instance, they sometimes take the twins of alcoholics and have them raised by nonalcoholic families. There appears to be a higher incidence of alcoholism in the children of these twin studies. Just recently Dr. Henry Begletter of New York looked at six-year-old sons of fathers who were alcoholics. Brain wave tests make it appear that these children have a greater amount of changed brain waves than the children of nonalcoholic fathers. So we're beginning to look at genetic markers and be able to identify those children that might get into trouble. I do not think there are any other personality traits or signs of physical indication that can yet be identified. Certainly a child whose parents are alcoholic sometimes identifies emotionally with the father. So we often times find a cultural approach or biocultural or a psychosocial approach where the child identifies with the aggressor, the father.

Q: Today there is more public outcry about driving under intoxication. The penalties seem to be getting more severe and more positive punitive judgments in courts and all. But from the standpoint of a doctor, who sees the excesses of alcoholism every day, what would be an effective solution to this drinking and driving problem?

Dr. Blum: They have a controversial random breath testing program down in Australia which puts you off at first blush but makes a great deal of sense once you get used to it. Police will set up a roadblock and pull over two thousand cars in a night in order, every single car that passes along that stretch of road—every one. We would find that horrifying in this country. Invasion of privacy! We didn't do anything, so why should we be treated this way? But it cut the number of drunk-related driving deaths in half in less than four months of existence down there. Controversial or not, those kinds of results demand consideration.

Dr. Gladstone: There are two major things that have to be looked at. One is the way we punish people for drinking, and I, for one, think they should be dealt with severely. In the Nordic countries, fines for driving under the influence of alcohol are directly related to the amount of alcohol in the offender's blood. If you have a hundred milligrams in your bloodstream, that is considered driving under the influence, and the fine is established. If you go to a hundred and fifty milligrams, your license will be taken away from you. Right there and then, and you would not be allowed to drive. Period. Any higher and you would go to jail. I would approve of that kind of control with teeth and predictability. Rather than fill the courts, establish the rules and let everyone know that if they are broken, the consequences are going to be absolute.

Q: Could a citizen refuse to take the Breathalyzer or whatever test would trigger the penalties?

Dr. Gladstone: The law would be that you cannot refuse. Doing so would be tantamount to admission of guilt. If you refused the test, your license would be revoked on the spot, and you would spend some time in jail. We have twenty-five to thirty thousand people killed on our roads every year. There must be two or three times that many who are injured but survive. The toll is enormous and unacceptable. To whatever extent drunk driving contributes to the totals, it can and must be stopped. Sorry to have become so animated. It makes me angry and simply should not be tolerated.

Q: Do you think, from a purely medical standpoint, Prohibition should not have been repealed?

Dr. Gladstone: Of course not.

Q: What about teenagers? Is alcohol or drug abuse more prevalent among them today?

Dr. Gladstone: I believe the data indicates that more teens are drinking more than doing dope again.

Q: Does that represent a significant change?

Dr. Blum: From a decade ago, yes.

Q: Is it a direct result of the increasingly frequent practice of brewers like Anheuser-Busch and Miller endorsing or underwriting rock concerts and festivals? Isn't that a pretty obvious attempt to get at young people?

Dr. Blum: No. On the one hand, it sort of reminds me of the beer gardens that I think were pretty nice in terms of having music and a couple of beers and relaxing. But what has happened recently is that this industry must have quantity to meet its marketing objectives. Breweries can no longer talk about just having a good time. Now they have to convince you to have the beer to have when you are having more than just one. That is what's so sad. And you know light beer is a great example of the attitude. They have capitalized on the success of light cigarettes, diet soft drinks, and all the rest of it. But light beer is little more than watered-down beer. What they are hoping you will do is buy twice as many of them because they say they have fewer calories. It is all a very funny game. The beer only has half as many calories, so you can, and better, have twice as much of it. They get you coming and going, teenager or otherwise. Oh, they also get you to pay twice as much. That doesn't answer your question, does it? I'd say what concerns me more than their sponsorship of youth-oriented events is the sponsorship of risk-taking events. The all-time great one was the *Los Angeles Times* cosponsoring an auto race with Winston cigarettes and Budweiser beer in August of 1983. I mean, it was a charity event involving auto racing, which is the most dangerous activity of young men in this society—the one with the highest death rate of any activity they get into—and it was supported and glorified by a brewery and a tobacco manufacturer! The grand slam of schlock and civil irresponsibility. Industries that produce risk factors multiply the sham by sponsoring events based on risk factors.

Q: Any difference in alcohol's impact by other factors such as income or race?

Dr. Gladstone: Both.

Dr. Blum: Lower-income people have more of a problem, and race is certainly a factor in that. Alcohol is the biggest cause of death in young minority males. Actually, homicide is, but the leading factor in homicide is alcohol. The connection is almost a hundred percent.

Q: I'm getting depressed. Let's move on to something else. Something light like depression or stress. Everyone talks about stress today. It's a cliché of our times I guess. But hasn't there always been stress? Didn't the cavemen have it, too?

Dr. Solomon: Well, I don't know a thing about cavemen, but I can say there have always been stresses that come with every epoch. Certainly people during World War Two had different kinds of stresses than we do at a time of relative peace in this country right now. But the stresses and the demands and the complications of life are, I think with automation especially, much more intense than they used to be. They are not any greater than in the past, just different. I believe the reason we know that more people are having more difficulty with stress today is that we are all more sensitive to it. We do not have to hide it as much, and people are less reluctant to.

Dr. Blum: Stress is an integral part of the time-compressed age we live in. But you see, what I'm a little bugged about is all the stress clinics that have been established lately. It is sort of like saying, "Let's put some iodine on that severed arm." Might be a bit too gruesome an analogy. How about Merthiolate on an open wound that could use some sewing? If the boss is demanding that you sell and you have to go out there and sell and you identify that you are under stress and go to a stress clinic somewhere, what are they going to do? Teach you how to count to ten like Ralph Kramden with the bus company. Or are they going to say, "Listen, we got to get that boss in here, too." If he's going to sell everybody down the river, so to speak, he may make a greater profit. But is that going to enrich anyone other than himself? To me, that kind of notion is a real problem. It is almost an aggression that is being foisted upon business people and many others in society.

Q: Is there an antidote? What is your friend in times of stress?

Dr. Solomon: If I had to make something simple and generalizable, I'd say communicating what you are feeling inside to some other person who cares is the first step in terms of antidote.

Q: I saw a couple in a restaurant last night. They must have been sixty, and they sat there screaming at each other the whole time. The maître d' said they do it every night. Aren't they fanning their irreconcilable differences instead of blowing them out?

Dr. Blum: If they do it every night, I guess it must be therapy for them. I think you will find that psychiatrists and psychologists will disagree on this because the psychologists believe in so-called behavior modification. They will take a situation, try to help you turn it around, whereas the psychiatrist will aid you in understanding the emotions behind the situation. To me it seems to almost make more sense to just run away from it entirely or try to prevent it from occurring in the first place, which is even tougher.

Q: Self-help books always tell people to relax. Is enforced relaxation possible for people who are troubled?

Dr. Solomon: Some, but none of it will help those who are very troubled. Those who are mildly troubled and looking for a new way instead of a cigarette or drink may try and actually get short-term benefit from meditation or self-hypnosis or EST. I think for some it can be a brief, effective therapeutic modality. The real question for me is: How long will it last? Will the self-help book last only as long as you are reading it? Will there be something worthwhile that you can hold onto for the rest of your life? And if so, by all means. But for most people, those kinds of books are drops in the bucket for the kind of help they really need. Books cannot provide long-term professional competence and association.

Dr. Blum: I always prescribe that people take mass transportation to work and tell them they won't have to call me in the morning.

Q: Instead of driving and listening to the radio? Thanks a lot! Elisabeth Kübler-Ross—she is the one specializing in the study of death and dying—supposedly gives patients a club with which to beat their beds. Does that hold any promise? Should we form a company that puts ex-wives' or bosses' pictures on golf balls? How about having a new wife's face put on alimony checks? Is there any way to escape this stress thing entirely?

Dr. Blum: I don't know. What about in those Plato's Retreats, those sex places, do they have a lot of stress in there, do you suppose?

Q: Moving right along, what about the hypnosis cure for smoking, drinking, other bad habits? Does it work? Is it temporary or for real?

Dr. Solomon: I'm prejudiced, but I would say those who have been really successful on the basis of a few sessions of hypnosis have been ready to quit. The hypnosis might have helped put them over the top, but they were already motivated and mobilized going in. The outside magic and a little strategy for calming themselves was probably all they needed to give up the symptom. Those who are not ready and are looking to make it on the magic alone won't be helped.

Q: Speaking of things that don't seem to work, what about diets? They are supposed to be the single most interesting topic to women, more even than men. There are a plethora of them around. Why don't people stick to them? Why don't they produce?

Dr. Solomon: Same problem as that of the weekend binger we talked about earlier. They make a perfectly good-faith commitment, intellectually, based upon some outside structure, but they haven't made any changes whatsoever in their inside life situation or how they operate. So when they are faced with the temptation or the stress or the anger, they revert rather quickly to the old habit mechanisms. Because learning new ways of coping and new strategies for dealing with these kinds of things cannot be done on an intellectual basis, they have to be done through a change in behavior and emotionally understanding what is going on in and around them.

Q: We bombarded our children with mind over matter and other clichés like the golden rule but hardly ever adhere to them ourselves. Why don't we practice what we preach?

Dr. Solomon: I think once again that even in the past, when people adhered to the golden rule, they did so more publicly than privately. Unless you are feeling lovable, deserving, and worthwhile, it is very hard for you to treat other people in a similar way. It is definitely one of the old clichés you are talking about, but the only answer is, in fact, to do unto others as you would have them do unto you.

Q: So people need self-appreciation first?

Dr. Solomon: That and self-confidence. Freud said to love and to work are the ultimate dictums of good health. I do not think I can improve on that.

Q: Are women, as they are getting the additional opportunities they deserve today, experiencing the same problems as men who are attached to their work and their jobs?

Dr. Solomon: I hope not. I hope that women, because they have been socialized to deal with their feelings—and this is admittedly a generalization—better than men have . . . are able to bring into the work force something that does not change them. Contrary to the current evidence and probabilities, they may even be able to impose some of their sensitivity and receptivity to what is around them.

Q: I have something of an admission to make. I said earlier that I didn't have any expertise to bring to this party. Believe me, anyone who has spent the better part of twenty years arising at three-thirty in the morning knows from stress and depression. That's me, and I have some definite thoughts—

Dr. Blum: Imagine our excitement. Well, if you are going to get into the doctoring business, let me get into yours. Reminds me of a story (you know, humor is the only real medication that will ever allow doctors to sleep in mornings . . .) about Pablo Picasso. He painted a gift for an ophthalmologist who had cured a very bad eyesight problem Picasso had once had. He painted a huge eye covering an entire wall. In the middle of the eye was a very tiny black pupil and in the middle of that was a microportrait of the ophthalmologist. Maybe an inch tall. And the reporters who were there for the big unveiling of this painting—this is a true story— . . . were asking him what he thought of it. He had nothing to say except one thing: "I'm glad I'm not a proctologist." Laugh twice, and don't bother to call me in the morning.

Q: Uh, seriously, thank you, the rest of you anyway, very, very much. Don't know that we have done in any of the world's problems, but you may have gotten someone a step or two closer than another aspirin would have.

Dr. Blum: Aspirin. Let me tell you about aspirins!

Q: No.

Trashmouth 101

Quick, how do you spell *relief?*

Bet your answer would come as something of a shock to Roger Staubach's delicate sensibilities. Odds are it was approximately four explanation-pointed letters long and sounded more like a by-product of, than a patent remedy for, gaseous distress. Disney-colored lenses aside, when people in the real world feel the need to blow off some steam, they cuss. Make that CUSS. The real thing, the kind that ends with lots of *t*'s and *k*'s and used to be more or less exclusive to pool halls and Hoffa-Kennedy conversations. Nothing indicting implied. Cussing is okay, therapeutic, in fact. It defuses stress as nothing else can. Always has, always will. And the stronger, the better because there are times when "Aw, shucks" does not do the trick. Just ask your friendly neighborhood neurosurgeon or golf pro or anyone else who goes on occasional tension runs. For that matter, prove it to yourself. Remember the last time you dinged the new car or hammered your thumb into Technicolor submission or received a bit of unsolicited career path counseling from the boss's son-in-law? Stayed cool and recited some poetry, did you? Cannot be done. Major-league grief demands major-league relief.

Mark Twain, a keen observer of the human condition, understood the concept. He once wrote, ". . . profanity furnishes a relief denied even to prayer." Don't know how well qualified he was to make the comparison, but at least one other rather famous Missourian apparently shared the sentiment. His name was Truman. He had the number one tension job in the business awhile back and handled it colorfully enough to be known as Give 'Em Hell Harry by friend and foe alike.

One of his more memorable outbursts attested to the fact that they did not call him that for nothing. It was pointed in the general direction of a certain music critic who had been less than favorably impressed by one of First Daughter Margaret's frequent White House solo recitals. Upon reflection, Harry allowed as how he thought the self-professed expert might also be a pompous SOB with a tin ear and offered to rearrange his face. Not terribly presidential, perhaps, but it got the point across. Fortunately his private opinions of a few other acquaintances whom he made while in office remained essentially private. Fortunate because WW II might well have slid directly into WW III had what he really thought of some of our alleged Allies made it to the Embassy Row cocktail party circuit.

Harry's SOB line caused quite a stir at the time. Believe it or not, there was once a time when nickel candy bars cost a nickel, women wore bras, and calling someone (even a pompous, tin-eared music critic whose face needed rearranging) an SOB in public caused quite a stir. Most folks simply did not do that sort of thing. They hanged each other in public and made each other ride in different parts of buses in public and did several other arguably odd things in public, but they did so with utmost verbal propriety. Hardly ever, for example, did they smile and greet each other in public with "Hey, motha, you suck!" It just wasn't done.

The rules have obviously changed. Whereas spitting on floors and opening doors for females, especially if you happen to be male, are currently taboo, otherwise acting and sounding as though you were in the privacy of the Oval Office are just fine. A socially acceptable trade-off, we are told by authoritative sources in high places, but far more demanding of one's vocabulary creativity than in the past. Blasphemy, for example, used to be of more than sufficient shock value. No more. Modern rogues and roguettes need fluency in profanity, obscenity, scatology, and, ideally, a second language or its cultural equivalent to generate anything approaching a genuine rise.

Sorry, Emily, the rough stuff is out of the barracks. Way out. Heck, nowadays you need at least basic proficiency in Trashmouth 101 to understand most PG movies or postgame interviews with baseball managers. Of course, you also get at least a basic proficiency in Trashmouth 101 by watching most PG movies or listening to postgame interviews with baseball managers, so everything works out about right for anyone rich enough to have cable or nonconformist enough still to be hitting the local bijou every once in a while. On the off-chance you do not belong to either group, that which follows is a public service primer in remedial smut. It ought to help you get by in the real world. Forewarned is forearmed. Sensitive readers will almost definitely find it downright offensive. Parental discretion is therefore advised. To put it another way, things are about to get tacky.

For openers, *heck* is every bit as passé as SOB* or its companion entry in the ancestral slur derby, *son of a gun.*†

Essentially a milquetoasted version of *hell* (as in "Go to . . ."), *heck* couches one's true lurid feelings by minimizing the damning

---

*SOB is, of course, a simple abbreviation of *son of a bitch*. Extremely mild by today's standards, this particular derogation never did carry all that much bite in this country. To the contrary, it has recently spawned the rather positive *bitchen* in our vernacular. For tourists, however, it should be noted that calling someone an SOB still constitutes definite fighting words in those developing parts of the world where people invest less than 65 percent of GNP in puppy yummies and pooper scoopers.

† *Son of a gun* implies similarly questionable parentage. It got its start as English sailors' slang for *bastard* about the time Vegas odds makers were showing the Spanish Armada as a prohibitive favorite. Being an enlightened leader, Lord Horatio Nelson convinced the Admiralty to allow him to commission a ship of ill repute to sail with the fleet. Resulting consequences would often be conceived, carried, and delivered while still asea. For sanitary reasons, all medical procedures were performed at the lowest point of the vessel's deck, just below the prow where waves could easily wash gizzards and amputated limbs and the like overboard. The ship's largest gun was usually mounted right above the scene of all this action so it could be pointed to either side without blowing holes in the sails. Since paternal instincts did not run very deep in the tars, little nippers born into such circumstances were invariably dubbed sons of the gun. Pretty exciting footnotes, huh?

fire and brimstone intent. This, as most graduate students of behavioral science and singles bar tenders already know, inhibits the proper functioning of both pancreas and libido. Do not use *heck* in any sentence of less than fourteen more up-to-date and prurient epithets unless you would like to be immediately, permanently branded an absolute nerd.

Over the years and oceans both *SOB* and *son of a gun* have lost whatever zing they might have once possessed. Since their primary thrust was to mortify by calling one's heritage into doubt and since a rapidly growing number of American kids do not have the foggiest idea who got them into this mess (a trend likely to accelerate in future years), their contemporary relevance is iffy at best.

Nerd (noun): one who leaves a little something to be desired.

Nerd probably derived from the Prussian *terd* or *turd*, both of which are said to have had something or other to do with the massive dung heaps peasants used to pile outside castle walls in the old days whenever they (the peasants, not the dung heaps) were not busy being raped and pillaged by rampaging barbarians. (Avid students are advised to consult smart kids' term papers on the defenestration of Prague for added historic perspective.) Used in correct context, *nerd* sounds every bit as dumb as it does alone. If you wish to be consisdered a contributing part of society throughout the eighties and sound relatively hip in the bargain, do not use *nerd* in any sentence of any length, ever.

Hip (noun): Often used as an adjective by nerds who also think *impact* is a verb.

Taken literally, the term *hip* refers to those bony portions of the human anatomy found adjacent to, above, and on either side of the spongy mass generally called the buttocks or worse. While not legitimately smutty in its own rite, *hip* (the adjective, not the social comment) is more than hackneyed enough to qualify as marginally offensive. Besides, its description provides a terrific lead-in to a discussion of the infinitely more interesting . . . time out!

Tacky may be PG in tinseltown, but it still looks too close to Xrated for comfort on paper. Remember how comic books always camouflaged linguistic no-no's with a bunch of funny-looking squiggles and diacritical marks? Believe I'll cop a Beetle Bailey and do the same from here on out. Near as I can recall, the mufti alphabet read as follows:

$$@ \; \delta \; ¢ \; \& \; \Sigma \; \% \; ♀ \; \# \; ! \; \int \; \lambda \; £ \; \approx$$
$$\pi \; ^{*} \; \beta \; \varsigma \; \sqrt{} \; \$ \; +^{-} \; {}^{*}_{*} \; \infty \; \lessgtr \; \int ♦$$

Now where were we? Oh, yeah, the infinitely more interesting . . .

@$$: Noun/adjective/object of inordinate attention by roughly half of the species when utilized by the other half to overstuff undersize containers.

By far the most popular and commonly used in a long series of euphemisms, including *rump, bottom, backside, hindquarter, fanny, rumble seat, poop deck,* and too many more to list without appearing fetished, @$$ stems from the olde English *arse* (which stemmed from the old Latin *ars,* which no doubt once meant something to those who did not flunk Latin), from which emanated the equally olde English *scitan,* which was normally misspelled *shite,* which, in its eventual turn, found itself squashed into our very own contemporary triple-threat favorite . . .

$#!+: An odorous, albeit physiologically necessary and ecologically beneficial, noun/verb/adjective which holds the distinction of very probably being one of the two words in the language that can be and are used in virtually every sentence spoken by teenagers who are more than six feet from anyone capable of taking away their allowances, cars, telephones, video games, ghetto blasters, or, horror of horrors, MTV.

It is also big with dock workers, tenant farmers, district attorneys, stock market analysts, schoolteachers, housewives, househusbands, baseball players, poker players, horseplayers, candid clerics, scriptwriters, media buyers, and everyone else. This may be a result of such marvelously useful variations as:

Oh, $#!+: A completely satisfying exclamation point for any imaginable situation.

$#!+ head: A term of endearment generally reserved for close personal friends, parole officers, and, of course, actual $#!+ heads. The root word should not, in candor, receive all the credit. Attaching *head* or *mother* or *face* or the like to most fruits or vegetables would probably bring them to championship guttural status as well. (Just think of rutabaga's potential.)

$#!+ house (a.k.a. the John): No longer a house per se, this uniquely purposeful facility is normally, erroneously used as a point of negative reference. Dumb. Though seldom listed on realtors' highlight sheets, it is every bit as important a condo resale feature as river views or tennis courts. Its centerpiece is a grown-up version of your old pal the potty chair, now known as a toilet in America, a bidet in France, the WC in jolly ol' England, and assorted other things in assorted other places.

Traditionalists prefer *Crapper* after and in honor of its genius inventor Thomas A. Crapper. Nice touch. The man belongs on the same wall with Pasteur and Edison. Anyone who disagrees has obviously not spent much time downwind of medieval castles.

*β**β:* so similar to *$#!+* that we shan't tarry except to mention that it also comes from the olde English (those guys sure enjoyed talking dirty, didn't they?) by way of the old Latin, where it was *puppis*, which is such an outstanding-sounding word that we really ought to find some current meaning for it. Wouldn't it be fun to be able to toss a puppis around once or twice a day?

*β!$$Σ& *%%:* The latent reaction to lackadaisical diaper changing habits early on, it is more a state of mind that physiology. Like its counterpart from across the pond, *browned-off*, the phrase is especially useful when one is asked to describe one's feelings on April 16.

$¢ ≈ ♂@♀: World-class gross by any reasonable measurement but probably too "in" for you to bother learning. It might be back "out" before you do. No loss.

β!Σ, √*&,#@≈≈:Σ√, ♂*πΣ√, β⁻$$ʃ, ¢⁻π+, ¢*¢λ, and an endless array of other lesser shockers are available for the expression of our obsession with pudenda and genitalic plumbing. None, however, can compete with real biggies like:

% ⁻ ¢λ: This is reigning champ since way back in the mid-fifteenth century (before then boy people and girl people *swived* each other for fun and/or profit). The word's staying power atop the raised eyebrow list bears striking testament to the weight of interpersonal relationships. It also lends itself to infinitely colorful permutations, can be and is used as every part of speech thousands of times a minute.

Everyone seems to have a handle on an absolutely accurate inside scoop or two concerning % ⁻ ¢λ's origins. Most think it evolved as an acronym for *fornication under contract to the king* (which might have made more sense had the king at the time of its supposed origin not happened to have been named Elizabeth) or a legal indictment *for unlawful carnal knowledge*. These are such wonderful stories that the truth pales by comparison. The actual, basically dull root word was an old Germanic verb *ficken/fucken*, which meant "to strike or penetrate."

One of the strangest things about % ⁻ ¢λ and many other consensus obscenities is that they tend to be very specific and to transcend their meanings. Not all potentially dirty words make it on the street corner. *Fornication, copulation,* and *intercourse* are ready examples. *Swive* is even better. You could wander around sputtering, "Swive this," and, "Swive that," all week long without turning many heads. Yet despite recent all-out blitz efforts to defang % ⁻ ¢λ's impact, the word retains extraordinary power to shock, to stun, to silence, and similarly to alliterate the sedate set. Fascinating. Since neither the words nor their literal meanings seem inherently capable of pushing our buttons, it must be code that does the evil deed.

As $#!+'s recent Morse internationalization from .-. ..- ... -.- to ..-. ..- -.-. -.- attests, vulgarity is simply not what it used to be. Nor will it be tomorrow what it is today. No way it can. The idea is to shock or, at the very least, offend. Words, any words, can do that for only so long. Translated quickly into everyday, garden-variety jargon, the really juicy ones become victims of their own success. Inevitably they lose their punch and must, by definition, give way to newer, grosser shots to the sensitive ear. One thing is clear. If you wish to maintain your newfound position at the offensively cutting edge, you must anticipate. Do not waste your valuable time with current filth. Anticipate the next wave of objectionable raw material, and work with it to make it your own. Play with a few of its most likely buzz words, and immediately begin throwing them around in test situations as they arise.

Although a few of our sleazier academics are predicting a turn-of-the-century upswing in the popularity of earlobe, nostril, and navel one-liners, realistic potential in the area of bodily function seems limited. Face it. The body has only so many parts, and most of the evident ones into which anything substantial can be inserted have already been more than adequately defamed.

Organized religion has been fertile ground for centuries, but it is now also becoming somewhat overused and hackneyed.

Perhaps you ought to experiment with hybrids. Try something like "Hey, mullah, you postnasal drip me off!" or "Yo, preach, pick earwax!" Yeah, I know they sound pretty bland the first time around, but who knows, you may get lucky and eventually hit on something innovative and revolting enough to put someone an inch or two off center.

No, I haven't forgotten belly buttons. But I suggest that you do so. Born washouts. I mean, how far can you go with repulsive lint jokes? Heck (oops), I do not recall anyone even having accused lint of causing herpes yet. What good is a body slam that doesn't even hint at the antisocial? Not worth the effort it will take to think them up. Scratch your navel.

The mannerisms, interests, and life-styles of such outcast minorities as nationalities and old people and young people and poor people and unemployed people have been handy targets for trend setters over the years. Problem there is that nowadays almost everyone is old or young or poor or unemployed or some of each, so easy-touch minorities can be tough to muster. Know any left-handed Lithuanians or white Anglo-Saxon adult males? They are about the sole remaining defenseless types I can think of off the top.

The only other bunch with promising credentials is those whose formal educations have left them unprepared for meaningful future roles in mainstream society. I refer, as you might have guessed, to consultants and those Jabba the Hutts of the business world, strategic planners. You simply cannot get much cruder than *prioritize, third-quarter review,* and *bottom line.* Whew! Vomit-inducing material if you have ever heard it. That's a hopeful sign because it means there may always be a supply of repulsive certainties available for emergency smut duty. Here are a few of mine.

Handgun
Kill
Drugs
Cancer
Domestic violence
Rape
Mug
Steal
Cheat
Divorce
Kiddie Porn
Lie
Betray
Rationalize

Add your own if your stomach can take it.

Whether or not cursing is really a legitimate surrogate for the shrink's couch, one punch line ought to be fairly predictable. Most of our current hang-ups are utter nonsense. Sure, we ought to try to maintain some sense of dignity and decorum in speech and actions. No argument. But if our bodies and the things we voluntarily do with them can honestly make us more uncomfortable than this trash, obscenity as we know it is obscene. That gets my stress cooking all over again ♀*& &@≈≈!+.

9

Laugh Twice, and Let Your Doctor Sleep In

So this traveling salesman gets home from three weeks on the road and asks his wife if anything exciting happened while he was away.

"Yeah, we had a burglar one night," she replies.

"A burglar! Did he get anything?"

"Afraid so . . . I thought it was you."

You're not laughing. How come? That was supposed to be funny. In fact, it is one of the oldest, most tried-and-true traveling salesmen jokes in the business, and since traveling salesmen jokes constitute 16.3 percent of all the time-tested yuk-inducing material around, they usually can't miss. Maybe it was the way I told it. Let's try one from another category.

This fat lady says to her husband, "Honey, I think I've lost twelve pounds."

"Look behind you." He clucks mercilessly. "I think I found them."

Didn't work either, huh? Boy, that was the number one chuckle getter in the normally fail-safe fat lady category. You are a tough crowd. One more time . . .

The first guy says, "Gee, you look a little down in the dumps. What's the matter?"

Second guy shrugs. "Oh, I just got some bad news about my mother in law [two, three, four]. She's getting better."

Mother-in-law lines don't make it for you either? Okay, this is absolutely your last chance. Listen up.

Three clerics were discussing the morality of abortion. Taking the straight company line, the priest stated flatly that "Life begins at the precise moment of conception." The minister allowed as how he used to feel that way but had recently softened his position and now believed "Life begins when the fetus is separated from the womb." Tugging thoughtfully on his beard, the rabbi corrected them. "You're both wrong. Life begins when the dog dies and the kids leave home."

When the dog dies and the kids leave home. Get it? Still nothing? Not even a snicker? This is obviously getting us nowhere. What's the matter, don't you have a sense of humor? Prove it. Quick, finish these simple comedic trademarks.

1. "Waiter, there's a fly in my —————."
2. "If I could walk that way, I wouldn't need the —————."
3. "I don't get no —————."
4. "Well, excuse —————."
5. "May the sacred camel leave a holy relic on your —————."

Four out of five? Must be me after all. Sorry. This is too important to let pass. Humor is no laughing matter. Another effective stress buster available without prescription, it is serious medicine. Many of its leading practitioners, Richard Pryor and Joan Rivers among the apparent exceptions, think it even more therapeutic than cussing. They may have a point. Whereas ¢‾$$!π♀ merely relieves the symptoms of tension, humor can actually make it go away for a while by activating one of your most vital organs—the funny bone. There is, as you might expect, a big, long med school textbook explanation of how it goes about doing so without the help of systemic chemical intervention, but since neither of us would be likely to survive another big, long med school textbook explanation, suffice it to say it makes people laugh, and laughing makes people look well, feel well, smell nice, and probably live longer. Not quite as miraculous as a quadruple bypass but not bad as quick-fix treatments normally go. Good enough, in fact, to have prompted *Reader's Digest* to name one of its most popular features "Laughter Is the Best Medicine." Now, I mean really, if you cannot believe *Reader's Digest*, what is left?

Perhaps the nicest thing about laughter is that unless you get yours from some latter-day T. R. Finaglesworth by the bottle, it is one relatively easy and inexpensive elixir to come by. Procuring a correct dosage is essentially a matter of knowing what strikes you funny and putting yourself in position to be struck as often as possible. First things first: What works for one may not for another, so start by trying to make some sense of your unique sense of humor. It can range from a taste for Chevy Chase pratfalls to the kinds of appreciative cerebral nods that did in Dick Cavett's Ivy Leaguish aspirations toward network limelight. That is why there are ethnic jokes and farmer's daughter jokes (a variant of the traveling salesmen genre) and elephant jokes and knock-knocks and Tom Swifties and one-liners and monologues and sitcoms and crossovers and JAP jokes and Gentile jokes and satires and farces and dribble glasses and a gag full of other potential cures on the market.

Two or three of those categories are relatively recent additions. Here's how they work.

CROSSOVERS
What do you get when you cross a kilo of Mary Jane with a bunch of politicians?
A joint session of Congress.

JAP JOKES
What are the three words a Jewish American Princess never hears?
"Attention, K mart shoppers."

GENTILE JOKES

So this Gentile calls his mother and says, "Sorry, Ma. I can't come over for dinner tonight."

His mother says, "Oh, okay."

Same guy says to his wife, "Hey, I'm off the hook. Want to mess around?"

She says, "Sure. Sounds like fun."

Art Buchwald, Mike Royko, Jim Murray, Herb Caen, and Erma Bombeck are lucky enough to skip through life getting a kick out of almost everything. Others, most others unfortunately, have to work at catching a case of the giggles. If we presume you belong in the larger club, the following ought to help you improve your odds of improving your disposition. Falling under the heading of "Truth Is Stranger [not to mention funnier] Than Fiction," they are absolutely true stories designed to help you decide what is funny and what is not. No sense wasting your time with Kurt Vonnegut, Jr., or Neil Simon if your one true hot button is a "Road Runner" cartoon.

Which of these stories are funny?

1. An eighty-year-old man was once arrested in Los Angeles for vagrancy. Once downtown and booked, he used his one free call to phone the L.A. airport with a bomb threat.

2. Augie Butz (an alias designed to protect the not-so-innocent, not-so-happy, not-so-smart) might have been the loser of the decade, crook division, for the seventies. He thought he had hijacked a truckload of beef. He had, sort of. When arrested, he learned that he had cornered the market on a rather specific cut. Cow rectums. No, I don't know what one does with a truckload of cow rectums, hijacked or otherwise, but they sure don't sound worth going into the freezer over.

3. A Wisconsin farmer found a strangely iridescent blue blob lying in one of his fields. He didn't know what it was but knew he had never seen anything quite like it before and doubted that anyone else had either. Rather than take a chance on polluting the back forty, he carefully wrapped the glowing hunk, put it in his freezer, and reported it to police, who called in scientists from

the university. From the farmer's description, the academic experts decided it sounded like a meteorite or some such extraterrestrial oddity. Intrigued, they sent a team to investigate. Turned out to be something from the sky all right but not exactly an alien substance. The packet had dropped intact from one of a passing Boeing's, uh, no smoking rooms. They say the farmer has been flushed with pride ever since.

4. The superstar of the Supphose-hop set, Lawrence Welk, was so sensitive to his reputation as the video master of the malaprop when ad-libbing that he took to following his TelePrompTer cards to the absolute letter. Okay idea. Iffy execution. He once introduced a toe-tapping medley of tunes from "World War Eye." Guess you had to be there.

5. When asked if he thought his near-legendary imbibing was having any negative effect on his brain, pioneer comic Fred Allen responded, "I'd rather have a free bottle in front of me than a prefrontal lobotomy anytime."

6. During an afternoon rehearsal for his popular TV show, Ed Sullivan asked singer Jack Jones, "Your father was Allan Jones, wasn't he?"

"He still is," Jones replied.

Witnesses report that Sullivan came as close to getting a joke as he ever had and said, "Hey, that's funny. I think that's funny. Let's use it just that way tonight." Jones agreed.

On cue that evening, right after Topo Gigo and before the Polish National Army's dancing bear troupe, easy Ed jerked (people without necks tend to do that) toward Jones and mumbled, "So, your father's still living, huh?"

7. At Bela Lugosi's real-life funeral, Jack E. Leonard stared into the open coffin and whispered, "Man, if you're putting me on . . ."

8. While warming up for another day on the bench behind Johnny Bench, a Cincinnati Reds also-ran was approached by a good-looking blonde who tossed him a ball and asked for an autograph for her son. Seeing quickly through her little charade, the self-impressed stud decided to give her a break. He scribbled his hotel room number and a rendezvous time on the rawhide and tossed it back. Next morning one of the L.A. sports page's headlines read THIRD STRING CATCHER STRIKES OUT WITH SPORTS EDITOR'S WIFE.

9. During the filming of a movie about nuns, a stagehand sneaked up behind the costumed star Rosalind Russell at a drinking fountain and gave her a playful pat and a pinch on the habit. Unfortunately the object of his playfulness turned out to be the flic's technical adviser, Sister Mary Holy Water.

10. At the 1980 Democratic Convention, Jimmy Carter bellowed homage to that great senator from Minnesota and consensus party mentor "Hubert Horatio Hornblower!"

11. Back in the days of live local television coverage of events other than wandering authors' breathless flings through town (if this is Tuesday, it must be "AM Walla Walla"), Butch's beer used to sponsor wrestling and roller derby and other cultural favorites down South. The highlight of its commercials was a bulldog named Butch, which always barked on cue at the precise moment the brew's bubbles reached the lip of the glass. Well, almost always. One night they cut to Butch for his big trick, and instead of barking, he barfed all over the announcer's foot.

12. It was late sixties drama in the round at its socially most significant. At each performance's climactic peak the white hero would decry his inability truly to understand his black brothers' plight. "Lord, let me know what they really feel," he would bleat to the heavens. Then, in a suddenly pitch-darkened moment, he would race up an aisle to be smeared with shoe polish and hustled back to stage center for his final speech as a miraculously transformed black. A very effective piece of business until the evening a patron, who had spent the entire third act with his legs crossed in abject panic, mistakenly got into the act by trying to take advantage of the same sudden cover of dark to make a break for the salvation of the washroom. Thing was, he chose precisely the wrong aisle for his escape route and wound up stage center, spotlit, and half-zipped.

13. Hey, it happens to the best of them. Starring one evening in a piece of free-form puff called *Three Pigs in a Blanket*, Mickey Rooney made about a dozen unscheduled exits to the increasing chagrin of his ad-libbing support players. He explained at the cast party that he had come pretty close to an overdose of prunes for breakfast, and well, he didn't realize the play was going to have that long a run.

14. Speaking of breakfast, a gang of Borscht Belt headliners used to

get together at Lindy's every morning after work to unwind by playing one-up with each other's lines. One day Buddy Hackett came in, shrugged, and said, "I'm sorry I'm late. My mother just died."

Without missing a beat, Jack Carter was supposed to have snapped, "Oh, yeah . . . you think that's funny? My mother . . ."

The last one runs a bit to the sick side, but it makes a point. Most comics, the kind who make fun for a living anyway, seem to be Jewish. Think about it. Rickles, Berle, Burns, Hackett, Silvers, Rivers, Youngman, Caesar, Bishop, Carter. Even Sammy Davis. Yeah, I know there are exceptions like Pryor, Cosby, Newhart, and Carson floating around, but generalities be damned, Jews are funnier than most other people. No accident. As one of the all-time great stand-ups, first name of Abe, once said, "If you don't laugh, you die." For obvious, odious reasons, Jews know the feeling better than most.

That brings to mind, in authentic comedic style, a Myron Cohen story about the oppression of his people. Seems that one day Nikita Khrushchev was up there pounding his Florsheimsky on the Red Square podium for attention. "Everybody Russia gotta have radio, gotta have refrigerator," he bellowed. "You don't got, you let me know. I fix!" Little guy in the back of the crowd raises his hand.

Khrushchev says, "Who you? What you want?"

The guy says, "Levine. I don't have a radio or a refrigerator." Khrushchev says he'll fix that.

The next week Khrushchev is standing up there asking the same question. Another guy at the back of the crowd raises his hand. Nik points his way. "Who you?"

"Ginsburg" comes the answer.

"What you want?"

"What happened to Levine?"

And speaking of Ginsburg (yet another smooth segue), one of his relatives finally made it big and rewarded himself with an around-the-world cruise. For dinner, they seated him with a Frenchman who did his best to make things pleasant by starting every meal with a polite *bon appétit*.

"Ginsburg," Ginsburg would reply.

Finally, after several days of that, he got a steward off to the side and asked what the heck the French guy was talking about.

"*Bon appétit* means 'have a nice meal,'" Gopher explained.

Ginsburg was thrilled. That evening, he preempted the normal routine. "*Bon appétit,*" he toasted.

"Ginsburg," the Frenchman replied.

Then there was the time three traveling salesmen (told you it was a big category) stopped at a farmhouse and asked if they could spend the night. No, I don't have any idea why they did that. Traveling salesmen stories usually have a car breaking down or some such natural disaster in their setups. Pick one so we can get on with the story. Got it? Okay, so whatever happened happened, and they stopped at this farmhouse and asked for lodging, and the farmer said sure (this is obviously an old story) but said his spare room was only large enough for two, so one of them would have to hit the hay, literally, in the barn.

"No problem," said the first, an Indian. "As a child in New Delhi, I slept out of doors most of the time. I shall be happy to take the barn." And off he tramped while the other two went thankfully up to the spare bedroom.

A few minutes later there was a knock at their door. It was the Indian. "My friends, my apologies," he began. "I did not realize there would be a brahman bull in the barn. It would defile the memory of my ancestors if I were to sleep in the presence of such a sacred thing. I cannot stay in the barn."

The second salesman was a New York Jew who said he had been through it all. "No problem," he said with a smile. "I'll take the barn. You should make yourselves comfortable."

So far so good, but hardly far enough. A couple of minutes later there was another knock at the bedroom door. The Jew had also spoken too soon. "A pig! There is a pig in the barn." He shuddered. "With my heritage, I couldn't possibly sleep with a pig!"

The last salesman, a Liechtensteiner no less, cracked up, grabbed his sample cases, and headed for the barn. "It's a good thing my relatives didn't have any weird taboos," he said, chuckling. "None of us would get any sleep tonight."

Sure enough, a few minutes passed, and there was another knock at the door. It was the bull and the pig.

Told you "traveling salesmen" was a terrific category. Of course, that one has something extra going for it. It doubles as a pretty fair example of the biggest, baddest category of all humor: the ethnic joke. Ethnic jokes work because they are potentially great and potentially rotten at the same time: potentially great because they let you replace the Liechtensteiner with your next-door neighbor anytime you care to do so; potentially rotten because they let your next-door neighbor do the same.

There is, of course, a fine line between satire and sadism at work here. An ethnic joke that enjoys a laugh at life is almost invariably on the money. The same story used as a weapon, a way to hurt or imply inferiority, is cruel. The way you handle their humor makes the difference. Mick, spic, dago, wop, spook, and the rest can be fun. They can also be vicious. Your call. Go with love, laughter, and the truth, and you cannot go far wrong.

And speaking of truth (that's three if you are keeping score), three last truths about this happiest of all mental medicines.

I lied about laughter's making you smell nice, but without it, your world will be written by the brothers Grimm. You haven't got enough trouble already?

The other guy's joke is never funny until you yourself retell it.

Whenever you find yourself taking things, including yourself, a little too seriously, remember the officially authorized slogan for National Schizophrenia Week: "I think; therefore, we are." Don't know what it means, but it's funny. This is a sufficient thing to be.

10

Up Close and as Personal as You Can Get

Last, best, most likely to help you shed the stress and strain of whatever ails you, if it doesn't kill you first, there is sex. Life's one great common denominator, it is more widely used and abused by paupers and royalty alike than a DeLorean full of any other expensive hobby, illicit or otherwise, you can name. Really. Even everyone's favorite cover girl, Lady Di, and his regal imperial earness do it. Did once or twice anyway. According to most of the free inside information you can gather while standing in super-market check-out lines, that is how all those out-of-work Britons got themselves another liege to keep in crown jewels for life. Can-not get much more authoritative than check-out line browsing ma-terial, so it must be true. Cannot get much more simultaneously habit-forming and habit-breaking an activity than sex either. Ever try smoking a joint while smoking a joint? "Let's get one thing straight between us," the positive-thinking suitor said hopefully, "creativity is one thing; suicide is quite another."

So you might well ask, if this body-tangling business is such a big deal cure-all and so popular to boot, why is there still so much tension in the world? Two answers. First, most people are named something other than Xaviera, which means they tend to get so hung up on getting what they need that they depend on all the things they don't need to help them get it. Secondly, the rules of this very tricky game keep changing as you play. Successfully seductive moves at one stage of interpersonal development can prove to be about as appealing as halitosis at another. To have a chance of enjoying, much less winning the competition, take it as it comes. Probably won't help, but it may give you a comforting sense of false security.

PHASE I: SEX AT SIX

The battle lines are already drawn. They have been ever since your plumbing was installed back at the factory. At that precise moment you were genetically imprinted for life as either a demure package of sugar and spice and everything nice or a rough, tough bundle of frogs and snails and puppy dogs' tails. Uh-huh. And Betty Friedan wears baby doll pajamas and Michael Jackson pumps iron and Renée Richards made it big because of her tennis.

Fact is, John Wayne and Norman Rockwell and their less-than-liberated world view are not around in the flesh anymore. Oh, sure, good Scouts still learn to tie knots they will never need to know how to tie in later life, and crinolines still flit gaily at square dances, but all is definitely not what it was when it comes to gender. In case you hadn't noticed, your role models have been remodeled right along with almost everything else on the planet, including the social implications of flitting gaily at square dances.

Though adult boys are still called men and adult girls are still called women, neither set seems certain of the meaning of what they are called. This is confusing but probably okay because representatives of both sides do seem to be treating each other a bit more like people than like categorical opposites and deluxe vibrators of late. A revolutionary sociological development to say the least. One of the effects of which are already evident all the way down to the playgrounds, where the most valuable player on your big brother's traveling soccer team is almost definitely named Mary Beth.

None of that will be all that personally relevant until you join the heavy breathing crowd a few years from now. With luck, that will be the ultimately positive point. After all, if the differences between the sexes continue to narrow, the only difference that may matter by the time it begins really to matter may be the difference that matters. Let's hope so. If the two basic types ever reach literal interchangeability, we'll all be in some trouble. Not to mention extinct.

PHASE II: SEX AT SIXTEEN

Sixteen-year-olds' great-grandparents were absolutely certain it was sinful to have sex at sixteen.

Sixteen-year-olds' grandparents thought it was sinful to have sex at sixteen.

Sixteen-year-olds' parents were not sure if it was sinful to have sex at sixteen.

Sixteen-year-olds are absolutely certain it is sinful not to have sex at sixteen.

It is a brave new world out there. Not surprisingly most sixteen-year-olds seem to endorse it. They should. As a group, individually, and in their infinitely varied combinations, they are looser, psychologically healthier, and more open than thirty-six-year-olds, fifty-six-year-olds, and seventy-six-year-olds were at the same phase of youthful hyperventilation. Looser, psychologically healthier, and more open—yes. Hornier—no. The sexual revolution has been one primarily of attitude, not activity. Brooke Shields and Christopher Atkins types have been fondling each others' Calvins since way back when they were called breeches. Fooling around just wasn't talked about as much in the good old days. Okay, not as loosely, psychologically healthily, or openly.

All this is little more than happy nostalgia to the rest of us but is excruciatingly, all-encompassingly, Technicolor obsessively important to you lucky punks and punkettes approaching sweet sixteen. Suddenly sex is no longer the mysterious object of nervous giggles and minimacho sniggering. It is everywhere and everything. Beautiful. Frightening. Driving. Nauseating. Utterly dominating. A persistent tickle that, with any luck at all, simply won't go away. Don't worry. You couldn't shake it if you wanted to, as obviously isn't very likely. So don't get tense when you feel yourself getting tense. That is supposed to happen. Go with the flow, and within reason, enjoy yourself. But be careful. You have a good thing going. It would be a shame to screw it up by pressing the procreation game restart button before you were ready to assume responsibilities and mortgages and all the other grown-up headaches. You can improve your odds by recognizing and anticipating a few of the emotional pitfalls the rest of us have already more or less survived. Things like:

PUPPY LOVE: Innocent and usually incredibly painful, it has almost nothing to do with puppies. It has to do with wimpy kids on the playground and tomboys next door whom you have just noticed are not wimpy kids or tomboys anymore.

BROKEN HEARTS: The direct, all but inevitable results of puppy loves. You will be stricken by a minimum of twelve. You will absolutely, totally die from every one of them. They are incurable but somewhat easier to take with each new attack.

FORMATIVE EXPERIENCES: Terrific growth opportunities. In order not to miss any, be sure to have a roll of Certs or Life Savers handy at all times. These work better than Binaca because they are quiet and lend themselves to pregame calisthenics.

SLOW DANCING: Just barely formative. Pleasant enough but somewhat limited in potential because of its normally public setting.

PETTING: Another good one unless you fall prey to that ultimate bane of teens and most adult males everywhere: bra snaps.

WET DREAMS: Usually direct results of either having or not having formative experiences. Actually something of a misnomer. "Sticky" is a more accurate description.

FRENCH KISSES: At first they sound kind of gross. If you do them right, they stay that way. This is where the little round things in your pocket (not *those* little round things in your pocket . . . don't be so precocious) begin to show their superiority in the clinches. As an icebreaker, try trading them with an acquaintance of the opposite persuasion without using your hands.

GOING ALL THE WAY: If you are a girl, the decision is between you and your older sister's doctor. If you are a boy, the decision is totally out of your control.

COLD SHOWERS: Essential to males of the species throughout most of their youth. As everyone knows, there is only one effective alternative, and it puts hair on your palms.

DRIVE-INS: Great places to have some of your more memorable and entertaining formative experiences. What with their penchants for foreign films of the Japanese monster and spaghetti western genre, they are also culturally broadening. Healthy, too. Steam opens sinus cavities, you know.

BEACH PARTIES: Another excellent learning lab situation. Simply excellent. Basically they call for boys to run around pretending disinterest in girls by playing football with Frisbees and for girls to keep their hair from getting wet by repeatedly insisting that it is the wrong time of the month, which, though they will never come close to admitting it, makes zero sense to all the boys except the one who flunked out four years ago but still gets to come to beach parties because he has an ID. Beach parties also involve the rapid consumption, by everyone within four sand dunes, of the one six-pack the guy without a job or friends his own age brought.

FORMAL DANCES: Normally not as much fun as beach parties or drive-ins. Parents almost never take pictures of you on your way to beach parties or drive-ins. The ones called proms are occasional exceptions. This is because they occasionally last straight through beach parties at which puppy loves, broken hearts, and all manner of moderately excruciating, all-encompassing, Technicolor obsessions have been known to occur within the space of a few deliriously formative hours. On the eves of these occasions, parents' Polaroids often record something dramatically different from what the beaming old folks have in mind. Whoever called proms a coming of age had been to one or more proms.

FAVORITE SONGS: Essential accompaniment to the proper execution of everything else. Fortunately approximately 53,000 of them are released every week.

GETTING PINNED OR RINGED: A definite throwback to days gone by. Very romantic and all that but not quite binding. Often used as the tie breaker in particularly difficult decisions.

ENDS AND BEGINNINGS: Again, be careful. Better (or worse, depending on your point of view) than half of all Americans actually meet the people they will eventually marry while still in their teens. Marriage is not necessarily binding either but can be a whole.lot trickier to escape than pinning or the other, lesser kind of ringing. Better than half of those who make the big commitment to high school sweethearts or anyone else subsequently go through an emotionally and financially taxing experience called divorce. Ends that become beginnings often become ends. Re-formative experiences are nowhere near as entertaining as the teenybopper kind.

PHASE III: SEX AT TWENTY-SIX

What you don't know now, you'll never learn. Congratulations or condolences as your night life makes appropriate.

Incidentally, do not panic if you find yourself having strange thoughts. Contrary to common belief, there is sex after marriage. Not that much of it, but enough to keep you going unless your glands are permanently overactive. And as the next phase will attest, it may even be good for you.

PHASE IV: SEX AT THIRTY-SIX

GRACIE: George, is it true that married men live longer?

GEORGE: No, Gracie, it only seems that way.

When Burns and Allen first had them rolling by their radios' with that routine, Liz Taylor was knee-high to most of her husbands, and George was still more burlesque technician than deity. Like most of their classic material, it worked because it rang of truth. Funny thing was, it shouldn't have been funny. This may not qualify as a Ripley-level oddity, yet it not only seemed that way but was that way. Married men actually did live longer than bachelors at the time, and they do now—an average of almost three years longer, to be specific. Data on gays are iffier, but if we presume they zigzag an approximately parallel course to available straight stats, one thing seems strangely clear: For the male of the species, lifework matters, but life-style matters more. To translate: Regardless of what they do or how well they do it, men who do it with someone else get to do it longer.

Moral: If you can find someone willing to tie your knots, guys, go for it. Marriage is good for you.

Not necessarily so for women. A distinctly hardier lot with or without spouses in tow, they get an average of 7.6 more years than men today and are expected to stretch their lead to 8.5 big ones by the middle of the next century. Fellini fans will no doubt find the projection replete with symbolism. Hard-core chauvinists will no doubt find it apoplexy-inducing because they generally assumed the gap would narrow instead of widen once women had equalitied themselves into the mainstream ulcer force. This object lesson in male inferiority serves to prove once and for all the thesis that assuming almost anything makes an @$$ out of u and me. It also suggests a timeworn social tradition women might do well to do without or, at the very least, reverse.

Yep, marriage.

Women have historically married older men. If life-span predictions are accurate, they would probably do better to make like Mrs. Robinson and try to drag some young stud up the aisle or under the covers. Such a plan would simultaneously guarantee better service early on and improve their odds of having someone left to fight with in the golden years.

This discussion is appropriate at this point because if you wait much longer to wed, you may be really old by the time you get around to being divorced. Get out of step with the trends, and you may be maladjusted for life.

PHASE V: SEX AT FORTY-SIX

Vitamin E and ginseng root are supposed to be good for what's ailing you. Of course, so are nubile, young, dedicated surrogates. Worse comes to worst, you may luck into one of life's best-kept secrets. Sex the act and sex the fact are not mutually exclusive. Hard as it may be to believe, some women and men actually wind up being friends as well as lovers. Tough combination to beat.

PHASE VI: SEX AT FIFTY-SIX

It gets confusinger and confusinger the longer you play. No sooner do you survive involuntary panting and get the hang of G-spot mechanics than the whole proposition starts feeling pretty mechanical. Then the roles mix together. All of a sudden the aggressor is the one who used to have all the headaches, and the poor guy has hair in his ears and . . . never mind. As the original Gipper or some such prematurely orange trend setter probably never said for publication, "I've been young, and I've been old. Young is better."

PHASE VII: SEX AT ?

Why not? As that great philosopher and well-known ladies' man Yogi Berra probably really did say, "The game ain't over until it's over." Jazz pianist Eubie Blake agreed. When asked at his one hundredth birthday party if he had any children, he flashed his ivories and chuckled. "Not yet." How's that for PMA?

Most Gray Panthers stop because they read somewhere that they are supposed to stop. Nothing could be further from the truth. Widows die first, and rocking-chair buddies aren't far behind. Besides, at any age, sex is sex, love is special, and a little bit of both ain't too bad.

11

The Battle of
the Bulge

Emotionally, physically, and even financially, avoirdupois is perhaps the meanest lifelong villain of them all. With the possible exception of cancer and bad breath, no affliction is simultaneously more common and dreaded in this country than fat. Most Americans will try almost anything to avoid its telltale ripples and flabs. Even in Hawaii, where dream wahines used to have their already ample charms enhanced by prenuptial force feeding, thin is in and the antiobesity business is booming.

From mountaintop to bayou and every social stratum in between, our collective pursuit of the European fit borders on obsession. As indicated earlier, we jog ourselves senseless, risking sagging breasts, irritated nipples, and displaced joints with every jolt, then rationalize the resultant agony as a state of quasi-spiritual euphoria. We bake and steam our big fine bods to the consistency of prune Jell-O, then plop them, without logical cause or intent, into the nearest available snowbank. We guzzle gallons of zero-based colas, the manufacturers of which spend millions to certify them absolutely devoid of nutritional substance, and go shopping in exotic, not to mention occasionally erotic, rubber jumpers designed to make us sweat like faucets. We vacation at concentration camps called spas, hang around velour-lined torture chambers masquerading as posh exercise clubs, and pump thousands of miles to get nowhere fast on stationary row-bikes. Some of us go so far as to mainline medical mush with our jaws wired hermetically shut. Most of all, we diet. Man, or woman, we do diet!

By far the number one topic of conversation in locker rooms and beauty parlors everywhere (sex comes in second), diets are tantamount to sacred quests throughout most of the Western world. Any worth the sodium they almost unanimously prohibit are recorded for posterity in minutely detailed, colorfully illustrated, normally counterproductive manuals that sell like the proverbial hotcakes they also almost invariably ban. According to the *Subject Guide to Books in Print*, the literary industry's official running laundry list, there are at least 1,000 titles available for browsing at any given lunch hour during which you do not happen to be otherwise occupied stuffing your face or trying to melt the rest of your parts into size ten submission. They include diet books that recommend enormous ingestion of protein and diet books insisting on its virtual irrelevance. Diet books that guarantee effortless, limitless loss in no time at all and a few that admit an ounce or two of difficulty. Books about the efficacy of low-calorie diets, high-fiber diets, high-carbohydrate diets, low-carbohydrate diets, grapefruit diets, avocado diets, water diets, ice cream diets, poultry diets, and seafood diets; diets named after each of the Hamptons, most of the world's natural wonders, and, of course, the Bronx; diets for rich people and poor people and beautiful people and even a quioxotic handful aimed at fat people; diets for teenagers, for geriatrics, for feminists, for chauvinist pigs, for gourmets, gourmands, smokers, household pets, cartoon characters, and sci-fi freaks. Serious diets. Frivolous diets. Fad diets. Diet books that make their concoctors' fat in the wallet, a few that have to do with diets that actually work, and some worth at least a cursory riffle simply because they have great titles like:

Doctor Romano's Megatetics Weight Reduction Guide
Fat Is a Feminist Issue
The Soap Opera Diet
How to Have Your Cake and Eat It Too
Sexual Nutrition

OK Way to Slim: Weight Control Through Transactional Analysis
The All Color Diet
Carlton Fredericks' Nutrition Guide for the Prevention and Cure of
    Common Ailments and Diseases
The Devil Wants Me Fat
Laugh Off the Pounds
The Tofu-Miso High Energy Diet
Luscious Low-Calorie Poundation
The New Enzyme Catalyst Diet
The Hollywood Emergency Diet
Dr. Honola's Fat Disintegration Diet
Psychodietetics
Confessions of a Late Bloomer, or, Wear Enough Eye Makeup and
    No One Will Notice Your Hips
More of Jesus, Less of Me
The Joy of Being Skinny
The Greatest Diet in the World
Tony's Tummy
Sex and All You Can Eat

And for a really great read, my favorite: *The 100% Natural, Purely Organic, Cholesterol-Free, Megavitamin, Low-Carbohydrate Nutrition Hoax.*

As the "best-seller" lists attest, we live in unending serial polygamy with our diets. We love them and hate them, start them and stop them, use them, abuse them, and never quite get in sync with their roller-coaster effects. The avoidance or attraction of things that fit into our mouths is pervasive. Publicly we forgive excess with euphemisms like *pleasingly plump* and *slightly chunky*. In private we do repeated physical harm to perfectly innocent mirrors and scales. Those of us who went to see a movie named *Fatso* ached with its title hero's compulsive gluttony and, by actual candy counter cash register receipts, ate three times as much popcorn as we do at an average flic. After a couple of all-out sets of tennis, we slosh through a couple of refreshing bumps at courtside. At the nineteenth hole we more than undo all the good of having flailed back and forth across the other eighteen. We pop raisins by the handful and chocolate by the bar in order to build up enough alleged quick energy to be able to exercise it away. We skip breakfast and lunch so we can nibble through Johnny's monologue. We pass the salad to leave room for dessert. We starve all week, then run amok on the weekends.

We are what you might call nuts.

Perhaps with reason, perhaps not—make that almost definitely not. Being overweight is generally considered unhealthy, unattractive, inconvenient, and expensive. But if such presumably credible observers as card-carrying nutritionists and doctors are to be believed, weight is not in itself as important as fitness. That being the case, on again-off again reducing marathons may very well be, forgive the heresy, somewhere between unnecessary and counterproductive.

Fact is, getting a torso where you want it and keeping it there are not all that big a trick. The human body is a machine. It runs on fuel called calories, which are invisible little energy globules each of which raises the temperature of one gram of water one degree centigrade. I frankly could not begin to explain what any of that has to do with your being chubby, but I understand it establishes the ground rules for one of life's hard, cold realities: Take in the correct number of calories for your machine's normal activity, and it will use them efficiently. Take in too many, and it won't. That would be bad planning because it would leave you with surplus fuel to cart around. Fortunately or unfortunately, depending upon how many mirrors you have hanging around the house, you have a built-in storage tank at the ready for just such a troublesome contingency. It is known as the waistline. Once it becomes the predominant factor in your silhouette, you have a numbers game on your hands, er, hips.

Here's how you play. Start with a great big number, like, oh, say, 21,000; then reduce it by 3,500, and you win. That is all there is to it. Take in 3,500 fewer calories a week than you need to maintain your current weight, or burn off 3,500 more calories per week than it takes to maintain your current weight, or work out some reasonably comfortable compromise, and you will lose a pound of fat a week. Not merely a pound of weight but a pound of fat. Break the formula down to a manageable 500-calorie swing per day, stick with it for several weeks in a row, and you will lose several pounds in a row. Unless you begin the game with more extra pounds than available weeks, your current weight and your desired weight will eventually come out a tie. The idea then will be to keep them that way. Again, entirely doable. Not easy but doable. Again, the numbers are key.

To maintain the status quo, take the quo you want to status and multiply it by 14 if you are female or 16 if you are not. For the sake of nonsexist reference and simplicity, round it to 15. Limit yourself to 15 calories per pound per day and you will remain one svelte devil indefinitely. If 145 pounds is the target, you can munch, slurp, inhale, or otherwise consume 2,175 calories worth of darned near anything each and every day. This is no doubt contradictory to almost everything your mother and Richard Simmons have ever told you about how not to be a slob. Sorry about that. I cannot be held accountable for your mother's or Richard Simmons's misinformation. From a pure and simple weight standpoint, it doesn't matter a wit what kinds of food or drink you use to add up to an allotted daily calorie total. Have a chocolate mousse fetish? Gorge yourself on chocolate mousse. Well, gorge may be a bit of an overstatement. Like Boston cream pie and mashed potatoes with mushroom gravy and most other consensus goodies, chocolate mousses (moussi?) run approximately 1 million calories an ounce. And that is for merely looking at them on the dessert cart. If you are heavy into gorging, which is essentially synonymous with cramming your face, you may be better off with a pocketful of carrots or pea pods. You can chew them by the bushel without plumping an inch. Some veggies actually work in the opposite direction. Takes so much energy to do in a stalk of celery, for example, that it counts as exercise. Unfortunately it tastes it as well. Can't have everything. The flat-tummy trade-off demands some decisions. Your basic challenge is to try to pick those foods you can enjoy both at the table and on the scale. Here is a partial list of available ingestibles and their caloric consequences:

Food	Calories
Anchovies	7 per fillet and thoroughly disgusting when used in anything other than fertilizer
Apple	80 on the core
	120 in a can
Asparagus	3 per cooked spear (add 4,000 per dollop of hollandaise)
Avocado	376 each (recipe substitute suggestion: try wallpaper paste—tastes the same and is lower-cal)
Bacon	43 per crisp strip
Banana	101 each
Beans	A bunch, and that is only part of the problem
Beef	Anywhere from 50 to 150 an ounce
Beef liver	Even more, but at least it tastes bad
Berries	90 per cup, average
Beverages (alcoholic)	
Beer	101 per cup except for flabby old jocks who seem to prefer their suds diluted
Wine	25 to 50 an ounce
80 proof hard stuff	97 a jigger
Biscuits	195 each, and that's without butter
Bouillon	2 per teaspoon
Bread	Anywhere from 19 for a breadstick to 238 for a piece of corn bread
Broccoli	47 a stalk
Brussels sprouts	Yuk, who cares!
Butter	102 per tablespoon
Cabbage	6 per raw half cup (No, I don't know why they don't call it cabbage slaw when it is mushed with mayonnaise)
Cake	You don't want to know
Candy	Ditto (if it tastes sweet, it goes a minimum of 100 a bite)

Cantaloupe	170 a melon
Carrots	30 for a big one
Cauliflower	28 a cup
Celery	20 a cup
Cereal	Varies in direct proportion to the number of cute characters on the box
Cheese	Another bad guy, at least 100 per ounce for the kinds that don't taste like avocados
Cherries	6 each unless you swallow the pits
Chewing gum	5 per piece
Chicken	55 per ounce
Chives	1 per tablespoon (must be why they put them in cheese)
Chocolate	150 an ounce, ouch!
Cocoa	177 per cup *sans* marshmallow garni
Coconut	276 per cup
Coffee	0
Cola	96 per cup
Cookies	Chocolate chips are the worst villains at 93
Corn	80 an ear minus dental floss action
Crab meat	136 a cup (seems a useless stat; how do you get a claw into a cup?)
Crackers	17 each except for the graham guys. Ready? 58!
Cranberry sauce	404 per cup
Cream (whipping or heavy)	53 per tablespoon and worth every inch
Cucumber	4 per ounce
Dates	21 each (why aren't Arabs fat? Perhaps they are. With the robes, who can tell?)
Doughnuts	240 each (thank God for the holes)
Egg	72, poached
	99, fried
	111, scrambled
Fish	About 60 an ounce
Frankfurter	139 (don't ask what's in 'em)

Food	Calories
Fruit cocktail	90 per cup for the fruit; 90 more for syrup
Garlic	4 per clove (eat enough, and it won't matter how chubby you get; you'll have plenty of room)
Gelatin	145 a cup
Grapefruit	90 each
Grapes	3 each
Ham	60 per ounce
Honey	64 per tablespoon
Ice cream	
10 percent butterfat	260 a scoop
Ice milk	177 a cup
Soft-serve	266 a whatever
Jam or jelly	50 a splush
Ketchup	16 per tablespoon
Lamb	60 an ounce
Lemon	20
Lemonade	110 a glass
Lemon juice	4 per pucker
Lettuce	40 a head
Luncheon meat	
Boiled ham	66 per slice
Bologna	79 per slice
Salami	88 per slice
Macaroni	166 a cup
Margarine	102 a tablespoon
Marshmallows	90 per ounce
Milk	159 a cup
Condensed	982 a cup! (now you know why it comes in such small cans)
Mushrooms	20 a cup
Mustard	12 per tablespoon
Nectarine	88
Noodles	200 a cup
Nuts	60 or so a tablespoon except for the little green guys from Ayotollahland, which run 180 Nuts!
Olives	4 each (it's the gin that's fattening)

Onions	60 a cup
Orange	64
Oysters	68 an ounce and supposedly worth their weight in inter-personal relations prowess
Pancakes	130 each without the goo
Parsley	2 per ounce
Peanut butter	94 a dip (though I, for one, have no idea how large a dip of peanut butter might be)
Peas	114 a cup
Peppers, green	32 a cup
Pickle relish	21 per dollop
Pie	
Apple	424 per slice
Blueberry	439 per slice
Cherry	485 per slice
Lemon meringue	410 per slice
Mincemeat	565 per slice
Pumpkin	304 per slice
Plums	6 each (and if you wait until they are prunes, the calories won't be around long enough to count)
Pomegranate	97 per messy outing
Popcorn	23 per cup *sans* butter or salt
Pork	60 per ounce
Potato chips	At least 12 each
Potatoes	145 baked and plain; the sky is the limit for other per-mutations
Prune juice	197 per cup
Pudding	750 (average) cup
Radishes	1 each
Raisins	419 per cup
Rice	200 per cup
Salad dressing	
Blue cheese	76 per tablespoon
French	66 per tablespoon
Italian	83 per tablespoon
Mayonnaise	101 per tablespoon
Russian	74 per tablespoon
Thousand Island	80 per tablespoon
Sauerkraut	42 per cup
Scallops	33 per ounce
Sherbet	260 per cup

Food	Calories
Shrimp	33 per ounce
Soups	Anyone's guess
Spinach	46 per cup
Tartar sauce	74 per tablespoon
Tea	0 as your taste buds will attest
Tomato	27
Turkey	50 per ounce
Vinegar	2 per tablespoon
Waffle	734
Water chestnuts	11 each
Watermelon	111 per wedge
Yogurt	121 a cup plain; double it with fruit
Zwieback	30 per piece

All this is interesting enough but hardly as relevant as it might have been forty or fifty years ago, when people ate more parsnips and zwieback (whatever he, she, or it might be) than Twinkies and pizza. Without editorial comment on the relative efficacy of our changing culinary propensities, this next smorgasbord features somewhat more contemporary delicacies (translation: junk food) and their respective calories counts.

Food	Calories
Arby's	
Junior roast beef	240
Roast beef	429
Super roast beef	705
Turkey	402
Arthur Treacher's	
Three-piece dinner	1,100
Baskin-Robbins	
single scoop/sugar cone	
Chocolate fudge	229
French vanilla	217
Rocky road	204
Butter pecan	195
Chocolate mint	189
Jamocha almond fudge	200

Strawberry	168
Mango sherbet	132
Burger Chef	
Hamburger	250
Double	325
Super Chef	530
Big Chef	535
French fries	240
Milk shake	310
Burger King	
Whopper	630
Whopper Junior	285
Hamburger	252
Hot dog	271
Whaler	744
French fries	220
Milk shake	365
Colonel Sanders Kentucky	
Fried Chicken	
Fifteen-piece bucket	3,300
One drumstick	220
Three-piece original dinner	830
Dairy Queen	
Small dipped cone	160
Large dipped cone	450
Small sundae	190
Large sundae	430
Large malt	830
Dilly Bar	240
Dunkin Donuts	
Plain cake doughnut	240
Honey-dipped	260 (add 50 for goo in the middle or on top)
Hardee's	
Huskie Deluxe	525
Huskie Junior	430
French fries	155
Apple turnover	290
Howard Johnson's	
Small cone	186
Large cone	370
Fried clams (order)	357
McDonald's	
Egg McMuffin	312
Chicken McNugget	55 per McCluck
Hamburger	249

Food	Calories
Double	350
Quarter Pounder	414
With cheese	521
Big Mac	557
Filet-o-Fish	406
French fries	215
Apple pie	265
Milk shake	317
Pizza Hut	
Thirteen-inch-thick crust basic cheese pizza	1,800
White Castle	
Slider	164
With cheese	198
French fries	219
Onion rings	341
Milk shake	213

The bad news almost jumps right off the page. You are what you eat, and fast food is fat food. Stay calm. Do not panic. You are not necessarily faced with the imminent terror of total withdrawal. Not only will certain junk foods probably not kill you, but they may actually do you some good. I once heard a credible-sounding medical type describe Big Macs as almost perfectly balanced meals. If the guy knew what he was talking about, and I, for one, certainly hope he did, we can indulge our Mac attacks indefinitely without guilt. This is because, as anyone who remembers *Dick and Jane* knows, balanced meals are downright essential ingredients in a well-rounded diet, which, in turn, is crucial to the maintenance of strong teeth and bones and several other parts of the human machine.

Quick, what are the four basic food groups we are supposed to balance to keep our tummies happy? Shame on you. Spot and Puff would be crushed. So would Leonard Gross. Along with Laurence E. Morehouse, the UCLA prof who created NASA's diet and fitness regimen for astronauts to follow while dining in outer space, Leonard wrote the rarest of all diet books—one that, if all those absurdly healthy-looking folks full of the right stuff are to be believed, makes sense. Entitled *Total Fitness in 30 Minutes a Week*, and the source of the 3,500-calorie-per-week gambit we stumbled through awhile ago, it has a thesis as uncharacteristically logical as it is effective and easy. Basically it suggests that getting into some semblance of shape is a better deal all the way around than merely losing weight and that it is not all that difficult to do.

Entertainingly debunking dozens of cherished, albeit erroneous, conditioning myths along the way (for instance, did you know it is actually okay to eat before swimming and to play Joe Namath on the night before the big game?), it somehow manages to make the entire proposition seem almost ridiculously simple. Eat a little less, move around a little more, and your skin will fit a little better. Sounds almost terminally commonsensy to me. But then, I have always had the sneaking suspicion that crash, smash, wham-bam-thankyew-ma'am diets, which contradict Dick and Jane's mom and dad's recommendations by leaving any one food off the menu entirely, probably leave a little something to be desired in the good-for-you department. And the rest of the notion is far more than suspicion.

Fact is, people do not really want to "lose weight" when they plunge into the newest can't-miss craze. They want to wind up painlessly looking like someone on a magazine cover. No, not Alfred E. Newman. The Tom Selleck/Christie Brinkley type is more what they have in mind. Deep down they want to be loved, but they will happily settle for some oogling and blatant envy. Since they witness a great deal of advertising, they think becoming incredibly skinny will help. Not so. Dieting alone simply will not, cannot get the job done. At best, it loosens bathing suits. At worst, it turns into anorexia. To pull it off without hurting, maybe killing yourself, you have to fix up what you have left. That calls for some attention to such satellite issues as nutrition and muscle tone. The latter calls for exercise.

Now don't go getting all clammy. Rolling over in bed is exercise. Listening to the radio is exercise (it is also a sure sign of genius intellect, but that is another story). Smiling at someone is exercise. So are brushing teeth, tying shoes, and eating. Really, even eating counts. Move anything at all, and you are exercising. Do it with any degree of frequency or exertion, and you will begin losing or, better yet, redistributing weight, turning fat into, would you believe, muscle. How much, how often, how quickly are your call. In their book, Messrs. Morehouse and Gross advise a reasonable, controlled, realistic amount every other day or so in tandem with the 500-calorie-a-day swing. Nothing exotic or even very strenuous. Just ten minutes or so of turning your head, stretching your arms, and getting the, one hopes, not too old and battered pump working at recommended pulse rates. I could condense the whole program, but then you might not exercise on over to the bookstore or library for a book. That would be a shame and a mistake.

Enough unsolicited testimonial and lofty theory. Let's get back to basics. If calories can be precisely counted on the way in, it follows that they can also be subtracted in predictable chunks. Every food adds an exact number of calories. Every activity deducts them just as absolutely. Sleeping, for widespread favorite reference point, scratches a snappy 2 calories an hour. That obviously will not take you very far, very fast without a companion intake plan. Neither will anything else. For the proof, check what you would have to go through to shed that magic pound of fat on effort alone. To lose the caloric equivalent of a pound, you would have to:

THINK strenuously for 3 months.

SEW, STAND, CROCHET, WRITE, or EAT for 160 hours.

USE an ELECTRIC VIBRATOR for 375 fifteen-minute periods (and no one is that randy).

DO ORDINARY OFFICE OR HOUSEHOLD WORK for 11 eight-hour days.

SING ALOUD or PLAY THE PIANO for 77 hours.

WALK 144 miles.

DRIVE A CAR across the country.

PLAY BACK-UP GUITAR at 22 consecutive Willie Nelson concerts. (If you do not happen to play guitar, you could accomplish the same results by going to 22 consecutive Willie Nelson concerts.) That man works hard enough for both of you.

LAY 14,371 BRICKS.

POUND 2,000 NAILS, SAW WOOD for 8 hours, and MIX A TON OF CONCRETE BY HAND.

HAND WASH 150 MEN'S DRESS SHIRTS.

PLAY BILLIARDS for 33 hours.

BALLROOM DANCE for 120 consecutive hours.

MODERN DANCE for 6 minutes. (Just kidding. It would probably take at least 15 or 20. Flash dancing is the kind that takes only 6 minutes.)

PLAY 108 GAMES of PING-PONG, 5 SETS OF TENNIS, or a world-record stint of Ms. Pac-Man.

EMULATE NADIA COMANECI for a day or NOAH JACKSON for an afternoon in the fall.

RUN 44 SIX-MINUTE MILES or 130 TEN-SECOND 100-YARD DASHES in succession.

CLIMB WASHINGTON MONUMENT 50 times.

DO 5,714 PUSH-UPS, 8,000 SIT-UPS, or ABOUT A ZILLION KNUCKLE CRACKS.

Ready for some good news? Sex also works. It allows you simultaneously to heat it up and to burn it off at the rate of a pound for each 17.5 encounters of the best kind. Makes one wonder why Warren Beatty and Xaviera Hollander are not skeletons by now. No matter. An undercover agent named Minna Rae Friedman attributes documentation of this medical miracle to the staff of Swedish Covenant Hospital in or around Chicago. Dedicated to the proposition that people ought to "Make love—not fat!," their "Sexual Dieter's Guide" reports weight loss potential per titillating move as follows:

Sexual Activity	Calories Burned
Lust	11
Listening to music	
Light classical	3
Rock	4
Bolero	427
Embracing and hugging	5
Kissing	
Regular	5
Passionate	1
Arousal	5
Petting	
Light	4
Heavy	3
Removing clothes	
In winter	11
In summer	8
In St.-Tropez	0
Stagefright	0
Striking out	0
General foreplay (nothing fancy)	6
Cunnilingus	4
Fellatio	14
Achieving erection	
For a man	3
For a woman	83
Fumbling around	2
Finding a more comfortable position	17
Moaning	12
Giggling	8
Laughing	3
Insertion	
If man is ready	8
If woman is not	0
Intercourse	
Moderate	25
Heavy	48
Incoherent convulsions	60
Orgasm	
Real	92
Faked	40
Getting a towel	22
Pillow fighting	103
Spanking	5 per

Sleeping	1
Showering	34
Expressing thanks	6

Supplementary activities

Anxiety	8
Immature ejaculation	12
Premature ejaculation	2
Cursing	143
Begging for another chance	10
Putting on a prophylactic	
With erection	14
Without erection	15
Developing a headache	3

According to a couple of recent academic research projects, one done under the direct auspices of Penn State and the other from Rutgers, such extracurricular calisthenics offer the bonus benefits of combating the single most prevalent mental disorder, depression, and of keeping their practitioners younger than their years. Good deal all the way around. Not exactly the fountain of youth but certainly worth the effort both medicinally and as a potentially great new hit line for geriatric singles bars. Here, too, diet can make the difference because the right foods directly influence such all-important performance criteria as stamina and creativity. So much so that a few of them with alleged aphrodisiacal powers outlived the holistic "health food" fad of the early seventies from which they came and have carved themselves apparent niches in sensual perpetuity. I refer, of course, to bee pollen, ginseng root, and the ever-popular ground rhinoceros scrotum. Not as exciting as sunflower seeds or wheat germ, I suppose, but hey, if it works, don't fix it.

And that brings us reasonably close to back to the point. You want your machine to work properly, and the odds on its being able to do that will be better if it is in shape. Getting it there and keeping it there are a matter of common sense, diet, and exercise. Too little of the first or too much of either of the last may slim you down all right. It may also kill you in the bargain. Again, not the best plan anyone ever dreamed up. To avoid this unpleasant side effect, steer clear of anything too heroic in the way of reduction tactics.

Starvation or exhaustion crash plans designed to rip off twenty-two pounds one week are so impossible to maintain that their victims usually wind up putting back twenty-three the next. The basic idea is not to improve your body to withered pulp status. Do it gradually, realistically, consistently. Do it right. Do it by the numbers. You will look better. You will live longer. You will even be able to sneak in an occasional gorge of chocolate mousse or Grandma's mashed potatoes. What more can a civilized weight watcher ask?

FOUR:

Is That All There Is?

12
How to Do Everything Else

Once they get the hang of survival or reality or both, many of life's better players turn to the development of those satellite skills most likely to improve what real-estate advertisements and aging hippies refer to as the quality of life. These include character-broadening attributes like an appreciation for the arts and the ability to read a *Wall Street Journal* without knocking over the orange juice. Like striving and achieving and occasionally even excelling at such diverse preoccupations as shooting skeets, cooking sushi, understanding complex motivational behavior, and, most commonly, bossing each other around. A select few become so adept at their chosen specialties that they are conferred the equivalent of twentieth-century royalty—the title *successful*. Such status assures all manner of lifelong perks denied to the masses. Our political, social, inspirational, and otherwise designated pinch role-models are allowed, for example, to live in places from which most of us only get to scribble postcards. To eat what most of us cannot pronounce. Generally to have a better time than is likely at most Tupperware parties and aluminum-can recycling drives. Joining their elite ranks is tough but not impossible. It takes dedication, determination, innovative spirit, innate brilliance, social grace, verbal acumen, creativity, insight, energy, conviction, courage, and luck. Mostly luck.

Hope that last bulletin didn't ruin your day. You may not have to be all that lucky to be lucky. As one of the all-time winners, Tom Landry, is rumored to have put it in a rare moment when his lips were working, "Luck is the residue of preparation and execution." Others, who, less dogmatically, "Pays their nickel and takes their chances," aren't so sure. Hard to tell whose views compute, but there is at least one sure way to improve the odds. Get back to the basics you learned in fourth grade. Leave new and improved mousetrap routines to the dreamers. To succeed, simply figure out how the guys on top got there and rip off their every move.

Blatant copycatting is not only effective upwardly-mobile strategy; it's relatively easy to pull off. Established "Who's Who" types tend to be surprisingly willing to help. They volunteer for benevolent mentorships at the drop of a casually adoring glance from almost anyone whom they consider inferior—which qualifies almost anyone. Just kidding. Genuine leaders are almost invariably ingenuous. To prove the point, here, free of charge or obligation of any kind, are helpful hints on how to do some things you might find yourself wanting to do some day—from some bigger-than-life achievers who know how to do them and then some. Here's the first: You may do well to shelve your speed-reading tricks for a minute or two. These quotes are real and they have something to say.

How to Perform Well in the Toughest Job in the World:

"Someone once said life begins when you begin to serve, and I have found that's very true. That's when life begins.

"When a person is honored by the American people by being elected president, he is given temporary custody of this job. It isn't "his" presidency. It's a sacred trust placed in him by his fellow citizens. So in handling this job I try always to remember I'm here to serve and that the presidency is a trust placed in me. Remembering those things makes me determined never to let the American people down.

"However tough this job may get at times, I take comfort, faith and strength from the American people. Americans are an optimistic, vigorous people, like no other people on earth. They remind me that in this country, anything and everything is possible. We are a Nation of doers, not complainers or hand-wringers. With will and energy and faith, there's nothing Americans can't do."

—RONALD REAGAN
President

How to Stay More Beautiful at Sixty than Most Are at Twenty:

"Practice voodoo, honey."

—LENA HORNE
Star

How to Hold Your Own with Celebrities:

"I am uniquely qualified to share my wisdom about interviewng celebrities. After all, I've interviewed hundreds of celebrities and, of course, I'm one myself.

"Celebrity interviewers should be well versed in celebrity neuroses. This is a rare disease known only to two kinds of people: those who are famous, and those who think they are.

"What makes celebrities neurotic is the ever-present anxiety about how famous they really are. On the celebrity Ten-scale, Sinatra is a **Ten**. A **One** is the traffic reporter on an FM radio station in a medium-size market. The worst curse of celebrityhood is the agonizing effort all celebrities make to determine their places on the scale.

"Just when you think you've got a shot at **Six**, your show is cancelled and your wife tells you to take out the garbage. . . ."

—PHIL DONAHUE
Celebrity

How to Clean Up with Soaps:

"Spend years of research on loving, being loved, making love, on people, emotions, and feelings. Be born with a virile imagination. Then the hardest job of all—learn to type."
—BILL BELL
Creator, Executive Producer, Head Writer,
"The Young and the Restless"

How to Drive a Car Safely at 200 mph:

"The same way you do at twenty. Keep your eyes and ears open. Pay attention to everything around you. Be prepared to take defensive action at any time. And keep your hands as close as possible to three and nine o'clock on the wheel. Do all of that and all you will need is a million-dollar car that can go two hundred miles an hour."
—RICK MEARS
Driver of the Penzoil Z-7
1984 Winner of the Indy 500

". . . Remember, there are only fourteen **Tens** in the whole world. The interviewer's biggest challenge is handling the fourteen hundred who think they're **Tens**. I have never featured a **Ten** on my show. I met one once, but he didn't recognize me. . . ."
—PHIL DONAHUE
TV Star

How to Solve Others' Problems While Working on Your Own:

"Pray a lot!"
—ANN LANDERS
Syndicated Big Sister

How to Tell a Joke:

"If you cannot create the material, buy it or steal it. Most important, tell it in twenty-five seconds or less."
—BOB HOPE
Golfer, Santa, Citizen

How to Keep Your Head Screwed on Straight While Living a Dream:

"Keep it in perspective. Don't dwell on past success. Go out every day and do what you have to do as well as you can do it."
—RYNE SANDBERG
Chicago Cub—make that, CHICAGO CUB

How to Make $300,000,000 and Feel Happy, Healthy and Good!

"Set a definite goal and learn and habitually apply the essence of the art of motivation with PMA—Positive Mental Attitude. Do it now!
—W. CLEMENT STONE
Co-author of *Success Through a Positive Mental Attitude*

How to Make the Most of Being a Female Atop a Self-professed Male Corner of the World:

"Use the basic skills of good communication, fairness, thoroughness, energy, and intellectual curiosity. They are not sex specific. However, because we still socialize girls and boys differently, there are strengths that many women can bring to top management, including being more open about giving feedback, especially praise; being less formal and dictatorial; and developing more of a sense of consensus."
—CHRISTIE HEFNER
President of Playboy Enterprises, Inc.

". . . **Threes** are fun because almost all of them have been **Threes** for so long they've adapted. They know **this is it** and they are comfortable and seldom pretentious. . . ."
—PHIL DONAHUE
FEMINIST

How to Create a Rainbow:

"If in your mind you can conceive it and in your heart believe it, you can achieve it. It's not your aptitude but your attitude that determines your altitude with a little intestinal fortitude."

—REV. JESSE JACKSON

How to Win in Vegas:

"Go to those gourmet dinners because the price is right. Go to the shows because they are the greatest in the world. Go out and look at all the bright lights from a safe distance. Then get your @$$ out of town!"

—JIMMY THE GREEK
Prognosticator par excellence

How to Get Blood out of a Turnip:

"No way! The proof lies in the French proverb: 'He has the blood of a turnip.' Lifeless, bloodless, no guts. Properly prepared with a light sauce, however . . ."

—JEAN BANCHET
Master Chef/Master Host at Le Francais,
Wheeling, Illinois

". . . Eights are fun because they're big enough to intimidate you and crazy because they know they are not Tens but have a shot at it and are terrified they'll never make it. In the history of my program, I have had eight Eights. All of them made me nervous. . . ."

—PHIL DONAHUE, 8 TO 10
(According to Women who
Evaluate Men Worth
Watching)

How to Take Being Knocked Down:

"Inside of a ring or out, ain't nothing wrong with going down. It's staying down that's wrong."

—MUHAMMAD ALI
Champ

How to Write a Song:

"There are only forty-three melodies in the world. Pick one. Sing it like you mean it. Remember, you didn't want a normal life anyway!"

—CAROLE KING
Musical Genius,
Gary Hart's assurance
"You've Got a Friend"

When One of Your Characters Takes Off, How to Keep the Act and the Actor Apart:

"If you ever feel you really need one more belt, make it a seat belt."

—FOSTER BROOKS
Actor

". . . Sevens are the worst. Friends are always trying to protect them from the 'mob of fans' and they are almost never mobbed. Sevens need our understanding. Scores of Sevens have been my television guests. They have all wanted limos with can't-see-through-from-the-outside windows. They have rarely lived up to the promise of their promotion. . . ."

—PHIL DONAHUE
Prober

How to Turn a Bad Start into a Happy Ending:

"Don't wish for a different situation. Make the most of the one you are in. Experience. Learn. Grow from your difficulties."

—JOHN JOHNSON
Publisher and Editor of *Ebony*
CEO, Johnson Products

How to Conquer Fear:

"Eliminate all negative thoughts and put all of your positive energies into realizing that you are going to **accomplish this climb** today. Oh, and don't look down!"

—DAN GOODWIN
The Real-life "Spiderperson"
Who Climbed Sears Tower

". . . **Zero** celebrities are the easiest to interview. They are, for example, the million-dollar-lottery winners. The event immediately makes them **Fives** and they are so new at the celebrity game they often say interesting and meaningful things, unlike celebrities in the upper register. I confess to having escaped the experience of being a **One.** There weren't any traffic reports in any of my medium markets.

"Don't sweat **Twos.** They are so grateful to be out of traffic they will cooperate with any interviewer and do all they can to give actual answers to actual questions. . . ."

—DONAHUE
Interviewer

How to Describe the Thrill of Making Out Seven Alimony Checks a Month:

"It's like pumping gas into another guy's car. The whole neighborhood's cars, in fact."

—MICKEY ROONEY
All-star husband

How to Learn from Past Mistakes:

"Find a spiritual basis and marry your best friend."

—MICKEY ROONEY
Actor, Friend
(happily, not best)

How to Look Great if Most of Your Beauty Is on the Inside:

"Be the American woman with class. Do the best with what you have and carry your **look** with style. In total, individual features don't matter that much. Best to take ten minutes in the morning and evening to work at a realistic look you can achieve."

—Elizabeth Arden
Cosmetic Sculptor

How to Keep Smiling with the World Literally on Your Shoulders:

"Remember, the bumps and bruises that come from being on the bottom of the pile are meaningless compared to the roar of the crowd and the feeling you get from a job well done."

—Walter "Sweetness" Payton
Gentleman, Inspiration,
All-time NFL Star

". . . Don't waste time with Nines. They got there by refusing to be interviewed. They are not generally about to put their magic mystery in jeopardy by permitting you to speak to them. I had lunch once with a Nine. He appeared to have a genuine interest in liberal politics but politely declined my invitation to appear on the show. . . ."

—WHO ELSE

How to Get the US and the USSR to co-exist:

"Return to the three R's. Repress Raucous Rhetoric! Moscow should stop telling lies about us and our President should stop telling the truth about them."

—Herb Cohen
Negotiator/Author of
You Can Negotiate Anything

How to Have a Grown-up Relationship with Your Lover:

"Mature relationships require both parties to overcome the mother/son syndrome that often creeps into daily living. Both must confront their feelings of disapproval and rejection. The man must overcome the fear of intimacy and self-disclosure. The woman

must learn to be dependent without becoming dependent and to conversely avoid martyrdom. Both must **love** and **enjoy.**"
—Dr. Dan Kiley, Psychologist
Author of *The Peter Pan Syndrome*
and *The Wendy Dilemma*

How to Sink a Six-Foot Putt with Thirty Million People Looking Over Your Shoulder:

"Convince yourself that, if you miss it, you will be embarrassed **and** poor."
—Jack Nicklaus
All-time Champion Everything

". . . **Fours** and under have been the backbone of 'Donahue.' They're still hungry, have seen too many **Sevens** make fools of themselves, and are usually wise enough not to preach. I also identify with **Fours.** I know what it's like to be a **Three** and a **Two.**

"**Fives,** on the other hand, have probably been too common an attraction. No celebrity can hold mid-scale status very long, and they are so distracted by the fear of moving in the wrong direction that they have trouble focusing. My staff has been instructed to wait until available **Fives** move either up or down a notch before booking. . . ."
—If you don't know by now . . .

How to Keep Going When You Feel Like Dropping:

"Stop. Sit down. Reevaluate your goals. If they are valid and you are willing to ask the Lord for some additional strength, you will have all the motivation you will ever need."
—Jim Ryun
Distance Runner
Author of *In Quest of Gold*

"... **Sixes** are invariably good. The best **Six** I ever interviewed was Dr. Reuben, author of *Everything You Always Wanted to Know About Sex and Were Afraid to Ask.* He enjoyed his **six** then got the hell off the index.

"I hope you do not think me too self-indulgent in expressing my own real sense of satisfaction at being a **Six**. I worked hard for it. I think I deserve it and I am not tormented about being anything else. I can honestly say that I AM A **SIX**!

"Right?

"Tell the truth, am I a **SIX** or not?"

As this heavy company attests, the biggest are also often the very best. By all means, take their lead. Not, however, to the point of settling for current standards of perfection. With fine tuning and diligent application of your own unique talents, you too could be passing on pearls of wisdom any day now. Not, of course, without some effort. Shortcuts to the cultivation of those other more or less—usually less—important abilities which you may need to qualify for anything approaching widespread acclaim as a trend setter are not so easily learned. This is because there are fewer acknowledged ultimate authorities on the correct folding of pocket handkerchieves and the like to emulate. To fill the resource void, think big. Consider the valuable lessons of collective human experience. To date they include:

How to Talk on the Telephone:

"I'm certainly the last one to ask concerning how to talk on the telephone—because in my routine there is never anyone on the other end."

—BOB NEWHART
Bone Specialist (Funny)

How to Get a Question Answered in Twenty-five Words or Less:

Don't ask it of Phil Donahue!

How to Suppress a Sneeze:

Press your upper lip.

How to Cure Hiccups:

Have someone rub the nape of your neck. This is said to have the positive side-effect of also solving certain interpersonal dysfunctions.

How to Cure Insomnia:

Read *The Heart of Darkness*.

How to Cure a Common Cold:

Drink fluids, get plenty of bed rest, wait a week or so.

How to Keep Cut Flowers Fresh:

Plunk an aspirin in the vase.

How to Thread a Needle:

Point the needle at the thread, not the other way around.

How to Become an Olympic Athlete:

Buy a luge and move to Puerto Rico.

How to Win at Trivial Pursuit:

Be old and capable of remembering everything you never should have bothered learning in the first place.

How to Start Your Car in Winter:

Move to Florida.

How to Breakdance Without Breaking Anything:

Be twelve, incredibly nimble, and any race except Caucasian.

How to Read a Map:

Use your finger.

How to Fold a Map:

Depends almost entirely on the size of your glove compartment.

How to Compute the Proper Tip in a Restaurant:

If you were well served, multiply the tax by three. If your meal was a meaningful experience, multiply the tax by four. If you are trying to hit on the waitress or waiter or both, multiply the tax by seven and offer to help clear the table.

How to Get a Waiter's Attention:

Light a match and hold it upright. If he fails to notice the flame, he will almost certainly react to your screams when it eventually reaches your thumb.

How to Get Asked to Do a Duet with Willie Nelson:

Have patience. He'll get to everyone eventually.

How to Look Like a Real Pro at Conventions:

Wear your name tag on the right lapel.

How to Kick the Coffee Habit:

Drink exactly one cup of almost any instant.

How to Tell the Difference Between Imported and Domestic Wines:

Roll the glass before a candle in order to observe color and tannin. Inhale the delicate bouquet. Breathe in deeply and gently swirl over the palate. If all else fails, check the price.

How to Combat the Heartbreak of Psoriassis:

> Don't scratch.

How to Spell Psoraissis:

> Got me.

How to Pick Sure Winners in Any Sporting Event:

> Pay very close attention to every word Howard Cosell ever deigns utter. Go the other way.

How to Shorten Your Stay in Purgatory:

> Listen to Julio Iglesias records.

How to Be Popular:

> Make lots of friends.

How to Get Away with Anything You Feel Like Saying to Anyone:

> Start every potentially offensive sentence with, "Now, with all due respect . . ."

How to Sow Your Wild Oats:

> Carelessly.

How to Drive a Dog Crazy:

> Say, "Do you wanna go outside?" when it's already outside.

How to Separate Democrats from Republicans:

> Carefully.

How to Appreciate the Finer Things in Life:

> Try the others first.

How to Live Well on a Teacher's Salary:

> If you ever figure that one out, run for King. The Presidency will never hold you.

How to Eat Spaghetti:

> In public—with a fork and large spoon.
> In private—with two hands and an old tie.

How to Make a Killing in the Stock Market:

> Buy low. Sell high. Ignore your brother-in-law's hot tips.

How to Solve Rubik's Cube:

> Get all of the same colors on the same sides.

How to Drive a Car in Boston:

> With your eyes closed and fingers crossed.

How to Drive a Car Safely in Boston:

> A contradiction in terms; cannot be done.

How to Become a Major Rock Star:

> Shave your head, wear your sister's clothing (your brother's, if you're female), get a guitar and earplugs. Optional: Learn to sing.

How to Play Winning Bridge:

> Get the cards.

How to Play Winning Poker:

> Trust everyone and always cut the deck.

How to Perform Successful Brain Surgery:

> Practice. Practice. Practice.

How to Put on Pantyhose After a Shower:

> Comparable in degree of difficulty to safe motoring in Boston. If you are old enough to remember the Twist, you may have a chance. Otherwise, forget it.

How to Get Rid of a Hangover:

> Ever try acupuncture? They say it can do almost anything. Besides, nothing else has ever worked.

How to Be Chosen as a TV Game Show Contestant:

> Wear clothes from your attic and develop the ability to reach orgasm at the sight of garbage disposals and cheap china.

How to Sing the National Anthem:

> Have an operation or move to Canada, where they have one most patriots can at least hum without risking permanent injury.

Armed with such information, Napoleon could have been tall. Atilla could have gotten better PR. Don Rickles could be funny. Chuck Barris could have been an entertainer, a producer, maybe even a living person. Well, maybe not, but you get the general idea. This is premium-grade advice. And here you probably thought you were merely in for an innocuous evening's alternative to counting cracks in the ceiling. Who knows how much you might have learned had you read the entire book this carefully? Not too late to start over, y'know. I think they pay us big-time authors residuals for that and there's this wonderful twelve-year-old kid who needs a new bike.

13

Rhesus Pieces—The Psychic Challenge Revisited

Learning how to Indiana Jones your way through life's gorilla-size pitfalls is an excellent beginning. Excellent beginnings do not, however, guarantee excellent middles or ends. There are still a googol of lesser monkeys called phobias and bad habits out there, and every one of them would like nothing more than to mess up your day in the park by hitching a ride on your aching back. Avoiding them will take luck, a head that is screwed on straight, and more than a little help from your friends. Since all of us are usually smarter than some of us, you can never have too many friends. No one, two, or ten will have any detour-free road maps for you to follow, but all of us—who knows? Worth a try. Here are a few more of the arguably useful insights we have collectively managed to pick up the hard way so far. Hope they help.

1. Watch for falling rocks.
2. Do not be afraid to excel. If you've got it, flaunt it. If you do not, pretend.
3. Give the right-of-way to all approaching elephants.
4. Shoot high. It is every bit as easy to fall in semipermanentlike with someone rich and attractive as it is with someone typical. The trick is in the reciprocity.
5. Make at least one cold call every week. If you do not happen to be in sales, join an aerobics class. Same difference.

6. Next New Year's Eve, resolve never to make another New Year's resolution. This will save time and tons of guilt.

7. Buy shoes that fit and bikinis that do not.

8. Do not fold, bend, spindle, or mutilate.

9. Memorize the names of every character George Lucas ever invented. They will be essential cocktail party chatter well into the twenty-first century, when we all shall race dutifully back to see our heroes with wrinkles.

10. Avoid foods that move without the aid of a fork.

11. Stay in your lane.

12. To find true inner peace, consider the wisdom of the yak. (A contribution from the Fairfield contingent no doubt. Wonder if they offer a minor in airport hassling at good old Maharishi State?)

13. Stop and smell the flowers. Also, vote for ERA if we ever have the sense to sneak it past Phyllis and Company again.

14. Do not slap choking people on the back unless you want the insurance company to think it was an accident.

15. Save stuff. Fifty years from now something equally improbable will be as valuable as baseball cards are today. Unfortunately, for reasons which may become increasingly apparent, I am not intimate enough with any dues-paying psychics to have inside information on what that something may be. As a rule of thumb, if your mother wants to throw it out, hide it further under the bed. Dallas Cowboys cheerleaders posters, smile buttons, and "I ♡ Anywhere" souvenir T-shirts are definite keepers.

16. Know your limitations, and ignore them.

17. Never miss Ann Landers.

17a. Never catch cold sores or put sharpened objects into your ears.

18. Learn to speak computer.

19. Do not worry about making change. By next Tuesday or so all money will be plastic. This will make Karl Malden happy. A laudable goal by any measurement.

20. Have your picture taken at the rim of the Grand Canyon, the Washington Monument, and Tiny Tim's grandparents' house.

21. Floss after meals.

22. Believe in something: friends, family, country . . . anything except your brother-in-law's investment tips. Most people—94 percent to be exact—recommend God. Half the rest are not sure

about Him or Her either way. The other half says a flat "no way" to Yahweh. Suppose these folks might make pretty fair candidates for Gamblers Anonymous?

23. Feel. Don't just think. Feel.
24. Use the right tool for the job.
25. Mount bathroom tissue to dispense from the rear of the roll.
26. Save a penny a day. Many a mickle makes a muckle. A lifetime supply of pennies won't buy much, but you will always have a real nice muckle to fall back upon.
27. Resist the urge to tell bomb jokes around airplanes, and never mix martinis with beer.
28. Always listen to your mother. Once married, always listen to your wife. If female, always listen to Erma Bombeck.
29. See Rock City.
30. Keep your head down, your arm straight, your body square, your knees slightly bent, the center of club gravity behind the ball at the moment of impact, and your weight on the left. Now relax, and have a good time.
31. Look before you leap, both ways before crossing, lively.
32. Stay off the grass.
33. Keep Christmas trees moist.
34. Chew each bite thirty times.
35. Do not call your best buddy Tonto. In Mexican it means "stupid." Of course, if your best buddy is on the light side of a load, go ahead.
36. If you don't have answers, have excuses.
37. If E. F. Hutton or any of his three-piece cronies ever speak within your earshot, pay close attention. Barring continued Reaganomics rebound, which seems a more reasonable bet than the big bang theory without a first big banger, getting by won't be getting any cheaper from here on out. What it is to be getting is, in fact, the outlandishly opposite. By the year 2017, for example, Onassis's heirs won't be able to afford much more opulent a life-style than today's mere Vanderbilts. Cars, right on down to relics that run on gasoline and have to be driven, will cost a million bucks apiece. A loaf of simulated banana nut bread will run $1,500. Even basic household robots and holographic battlefield reenactment scenarios for the kids will set you back a couple of grand. Hope you made the right call back in Chapter

Four. Put in your fifteen or twenty hours a week at the micro-chip recycling plant for a measly 200 or 300 thou, and you could be in some trouble Paine-Webber wise. For further evidence, consult your future shopping list.

	Today	2017
Paperback novel	$2.50	$40.00
First-run movie	5.00	80.00
Annual Social Security deduction	1,400.00	250,000.00
Quart of milk	0.75	5,00
First-class stamp	0.20	3.20
Six-pack of beer	2.50	40.00
Toothpaste	1.50	24.00
Pound of coffee	3.50	56.00
Cigarettes	1.00	Not enough
Beefsteak per pound	2.89	34.00
Coffee cake	2.29	18.00
Domestic wine	4.79	37.50
Prophylactics	Price is usually no object	

The year 2017 sound safely distant? Shows how much you know. It is right around the calendar, closer than the next moon landing, closer than the first test-tube male pregnancy, closer than a cure for the common cold. Too close for comfort, I assure you. Well, I don't actually assure you. The aforementioned psychics do. They can do that sort of thing because they know all about things that haven't happened yet. More accurately, they know that you do not know all about things that haven't happened yet and may not know that they may not really know all about them either. They ply their ethereal trade by quietly predicting approximately 4,000 future wonders a month, then calling neon-lit attention to the half dozen or so that coincidentally occur as officially divined. Pretty tricky bunch all right.

How do I myself know these unknowable things, you ask? Am I, beneath this thoroughly ordinary façade, a closet mystic of higher order? No. I simply spend a lot of time in supermarket check-out lines. It was in just such a setting that I recently came across the definitive compendium of future truths. Compiled by everyone's favorite plotless book factory, the Wallechinsky/Wallace clan, it is entitled *The People's Almanac Presents the Book of Predictions*. In its contributing seers' consensus, 2017 promises to be an idyllic time of guiltless interpersonal frolic, unprecedented longevity and good health, total communications, affordable sabbaticals in outer space, and seaweed casseroles for dinner—a very good year indeed. Their specific projections include:

Twenty-four hours of daylight through the use of solar satellites which will store and release the sun's rays on cue. Ought to play hell with drive-ins.

The black pope will decide to move the Vatican back out of Jerusalem. Neither Little Rock nor Moscow will be among the finalists.

The first total eclipse of the sun since 1979 will be observed throughout the Northern Hemisphere. This remarkable phenomenon will be less than awe-inspiring because all those solar satellites will make it impossible to see with the naked eye. Ah, progress.

A tiny fossil will be found on Mars.

Jeane Dixon will make her one millionth prediction for the *National Enquirer* or *Star* or *Midnight* and proudly note that no fewer than six have almost come true.

The Soviet Union will attempt to alter history by having scientific information retransmitted through time via tachyons. This may be a more worthwhile contribution to humanity than it appears at first blush. If they pull it off, we'll at least find out what really happened to Korean Airlines' Flight 007.

Fidel Castro's worldwide syndicated TV show will be canceled and replaced by Idi Amin Dada reruns.

Atlantis will surface.

And here are a few also-rans that didn't make the *Almanac* cut:

Rules changes will shorten the average major-league baseball game to eighteen minutes. Pregame ceremonies will, however, last three days to accommodate commercials.

Zsa Zsa Gabor will be ten years older and still banned in Philadelphia, where she once lost the hearts of the good burghers by refusing to perform until some elderly handicapped patrons were removed to the rear of the theater. She and Mickey Rooney and Elizabeth Taylor all will be wed. None will be able to remember how often they have already done that. Neither will anyone else. Their cumulative nuptials will become the basis of a national lottery, with proceeds going to a home for retired Muppets.

Elsewhere in the world of entertainment, Billy Joel will release his two thousandth album of greatest hits, and the Rolling Stones will offer their forty-third triumphant farewell tour.

George Burns will replace Johnny Carson on the "Tonight Show" when the latter finally gets so tired of arguing with the network over his piddling $3 million per show contract that he buys it and brings Fred Silverman back in triumph to clean the stalls.

The hundreds of critically ill people who were cryogenically frozen until such time as cures for their illnesses could be found will be miraculously thawed, then will die of heart failure when they see their storage bills.

A child whose natural parents have never been divorced will be found running wild in a suburb of Charlotte. Historians will eventually identify his mysterious weapon as something called a yo-yo.

Male and female astronauts will file suit against the Internal Revenue Service to have their taxes lowered to the 90 percent bracket on the basis of their common law coorbitation.

Houston and Seattle will still be trying to win some pennants to hang onto their domes. Both will still be failing.

Interior decorators will be agog with excitement over the *au courant* rage: houses without video rooms.

Van Halen will still be deaf.

As a result of their Westernized diet, all Japanese will be more than six feet tall and weigh 200 pounds. The island will sink.

Someone will repeat a recognition study first issued back in the 1980s. Twice as many of its respondents will still know E.T. as know the U.S. vice president.

The flying age will be raised to twelve.

Howard Cosell will be named the eighth wonder of the world

when it is learned that he passed away in 1967 but that an unattendant attendant was guilty of a botched embalming. I think they are planning to use the sordid details as a pilot for "Son of Quincy—Locker Room Coroner."

Victoria Principal will be forced to undergo psychiatric treatment in the wake of Rex Reed's exposé that a flab was detected in her last health club commercial.

The Dallas Cowboys, Miami Dolphins, and San Andreas Faults (né the Oakland, L.A., Bakersfield, and Encino Raiders) will tee it up in the demolition format Rozelle Bowl.

Jim McCay will disappear while covering World War VI in Nepal. He will later be rumored to have joined the Maharishi Mahesh Yogi's new rock band the Geriatric Wimps.

Tollway systems will pay for themselves.

Louise Brown will lead the fight for sterilization of all males and females over the age of three.

Every dog in New York City will decide to urinate simultaneously. No one will notice.

Diogenes will still be looking.

People will still be writing, reading, and being disappointed by books on how to survive.

Far be it from me to question such awesome powers or their origins. In point of fact, I have no questions about them at all. I think psychics and their awesome powers are a pile of unadulterated ♂˜££$#!+. To put it another way, don't hold your breath.

Seers of the world unite! Focus on 2017, and prove me wrong. The year was not chosen idly. It is the carefully calculated anchor for a controlled scientific experiment through which the rest of the population will be able to observe your magical talents once and for all.

The president of the United States who will be inaugurated in January 2017 is alive today. Tell me who she is no later than inauguration day of 1989, and I shall pay you about a quarter of a million bucks. Really. The day this book was published, I escrowed $10,000 in authentic currency of the realm. By 2017 it will compound itself into something in excess of twenty-five times that amount. The whole wad is yours for the predicting. So go off to wherever you go off to do your supernatural thing, and come up with the name. Once you have it, send it to:

The Pres—2017
% Wally Phillips
WGN Radio
Chicago, Illinois 60618

I'll lock all the entries into a time capsule at the 1992 Chicago World's Fair, if there is a 1992 Chicago World's Fair, or in Phil Donahue's backyard, if there isn't. The capsule will be set to pop dramatically open on the second Wednesday of January in 2017. If your crystal ball call matches the name on the door at 1600 Pennsylvania Avenue, you and your progeny will be able to savor the joys of the twenty-first century in style. Why, with all that money, you could probably afford a car! No strings attached, but ties will have to split the pot.

Incidentally, this is not the first time I have issued this kind of challenge. The seed money is, in fact, a rollover from my last fruitless journey into the unknown. I had a name hidden in a little black box for ten years. I offered a reward to anyone who could conjure it up. Plenty of takers. Zero winners. Only after Dale Arden's screen alter ego, Jean Rogers, made her appearance did those blessed with the force let me know that their failure had been my fault. My inferior efforts at telepathic receptions or something. Sorry about that. I'm staying out of it this time around. As I said, he, she, or it is already out there somewhere. It's worth $250,000. Call my bluff.

14
The Beginning?

"So what's it all about, Alfie?"

Is it just for the fifteen ten-thousandths of a second we live?

"When you sort it out, are we meant to take more than we give," or . . . did we slither out of the muck and spend 3 or 4 million years of evolution revolution acquiring these beautiful bodies and brains only to fireball the whole crowd into smithereens?

Don't believe old Alf ever came up with the one, true answer, did he? Don't know if he ever came up with any answers at all. As a matter of fact, I am not certain he even understood the questions. Lucky guy. Had he wasted his precious time down here trying to be as profound as the rest of us, he still would not have known if he was on the right track until it was too late to change course. When it comes to such imponderable secrets as the meaning of life, heaven only knows. Only who knows heaven?

Where is it? What is it? The Good Book says there is such a place: a golden city about the size of China (140 cubits in any direction, to be biblically precise) way out there . . . up there . . . somewhere. From what I've heard, it is supposed to be something special by any measure. In addition to providing an opportunity to thank the Boss personally for the beneficence and all, its brochures promise everyone's idea of the good life in spades, forever. Some have questioned its locale. Lenny Bruce, for example, once noted that the earth is in constant rotation on its axis, and depending upon your exact check-out time, you may actually have to go down there to get up there. But no one has convincingly argued its dimensions. If anything, they may be conservative. After all, there are currently 4 billion candidates for admission treading water on this planet alone and who knows how many lovable E.T.'s tele-kinesizing themselves around elsewhere. As if that weren't gang enough, Mr. Ripley believes that approximately 75 billion have gone before us to their just rewards for games well played. Well, played anyway. Last time anyone in authority checked, the average man stood five feet ten inches and weighed 165 pounds. The average women went five-four/126. Since we all are eventually supposed to have our bodies and souls reunited, there may not be much roaming room in the high-rent district once we get there. All this would probably be more bothersome if one were not secure in the knowledge that a master plan is at work here.

The way we other true believers and bet hedgers look at it, any supreme being capable of coming up with creatures capable of coming up with a question like "If God is all-powerful, can He make a rock too big for Him to pick up?" must surely be capable of finding room for everyone at the inn or, in a pinch, the barn out back. Maybe the staff angels and saints add on extra dorms every millennium or two. Another theory suggests they use some kind of high-rise stacking system based on seniority. If so, it would probably take a week's worth of crawling over cloud banks full of ancestors to visit Uncle Elmo and Aunt Martha. Of course, with eternity on your hands, a week here or there won't be that big a deal.

Now I would never have thought of giving Ripley a ripple over any of that if Carl Sagan hadn't come to my rescue. He put the amount of surplus space they have to work with up there into understandable layman's terms with an academic text turned TV show all about the universe. Have any idea how big the cosmos really is? BIG! According to Carl, we can see about 10,000 of our galaxy's stars from earth, but there are actually billions of stars in our galaxy and billions of galaxies in the universe. Billions and billions of them! I can't say that as well as he does, but you get the idea.

Have any idea how many galaxies or anything else it takes to make a billion? MANY! So many that, if you were to plunk twenty silver dollars a minute into a Vegas slot and never stop, it would take you 96 years to blow a billion of them. Unless your name is Packard, it would probably take you even longer to save up the billion to blow on the experiment, so why don't you take my word for it? Suffice it to say, a billion is a whole bunch. Enough to allow each of us to be assigned a cozy little star of our very own 10,000 light-years from Uncle Elmo and Aunt Martha and everyone else. For that matter, 10 billion light-years away. The *Everyday Almanac* reports that astronomers at the University of California have recently discovered a quasar or something that far away from our neck of the woods. To get a handle on how far we are talking here, its editors suggested that we "Imagine that the thickness of this page represents the distance from earth to sun (93,000,000 miles or about eight light-minutes). Then the distance to the nearest star (4⅓ light-years) is a 71-foot-high sheaf of paper. And the diameter of our galaxy (100,000 light-years) is a 310-mile-high stack, while the edge of the known universe is not reached until the pile of paper is 31 million miles high—a third of the way to the sun." By then, of course, the paper would have caught fire and messed up the entire demonstration. Not, however, before its point had been made. Outer space has more than enough of itself to accommodate heaven regardless of its measurements.

As if that were insufficient solace, you also have a choice. If, for some inscrutable reason, joining the harp squad does not appeal, you can comply with the requests of teachers, bosses, ex-spouses, and assorted other detractors whom you have encountered too closely along the way and go to hell. Your call, but before you make it, know the difference in ultimate destinations.

This whole heaven and hell concept is obviously difficult for us mere mortals to grasp. To be honest, the prospect of bumping around Red China for the rest of time doesn't seem as though it would be all that eternally blissful, but, hey, some other parts of the Big Guy's big scheme took some getting used to at first blush as well. I have never understood why, for example, women's buttons are on the wrong side or how Engelbert Humperdinck got to be so popular. God probably wouldn't explain even if you could get close enough to ask Him, Her, or It. Seems obstinate about not letting us in on any of the ethereal inside scoops until we pass through Peter's gate. Maybe such unanswerables exist precisely because they confuse. If we all caught on to everything right away, there would not be much call for Billy Graham and he would have to go into politics like Jesse Jackson.

All I know for sure is that reward and punishment play major roles in the big payoff. Do it right while you have the chance, and you win. Do it wrong, and you lose. Man, do you lose! Can you imagine spending eternity in Pittsburgh, in August? The ozone layers alone could kill you if you were not already dead. This is a high-stakes lottery. Enough to make you straighten up and fly right real quick. And even that horrifying description probably does not do it justice. The actual distinctions between final forwarding addresses cannot be accurately translated into simple human terms, but these feeble attempts may help you get them into comparative focus:

Heaven is where you are served surf and turf with a side of twice-baked potatoes, all-you-can-eat salad bar, house cabernet, and frango mints at every meal. In hell the grease in the french fry cooker is changed only once a month.

Heaven is an open charge plate at Saks. Hell is a never-ending race for blue light specials.

Heaven is being a sports fan anywhere except Chicago. Hell is Howard Cosell on every channel.

Heaven is a heated pool with attached Jacuzzi. Hell is a backed-up toilet.

Heaven is Martha's Vineyard. Hell is Martha's tuna surprise.

Heaven is a Beach Boys concert on the Fourth of July. Hell is being able to remember how old you were the first time you heard each new medley of their greatest hit.

Heaven is picking the winner of the Kentucky Derby. Hell is losing the ticket, finding it, then learning that the nag has been disqualified as a burnout.

Heaven is where the French are cooks, the Italians are the lovers, the Germans are the industrialists, the Swiss are the bankers, and the English are the police. Hell is where the Italians are the industrialists, the French are the bankers, the Swiss are the lovers, the English are the cooks, and the Germans are the police.

To some, heaven is a mountain; to others, a seashore, a penthouse, or a casino. To Kermit the Frog, it is a wet lily pad full of fat, juicy flies. So varied are our private dreams and expectations that only two things about the hereafter can be counted upon with any degree of certainty: It will not be here until you are after, and the only way to find out whose visions are clear scares most of us to death. There, I said it. Death! Boogey, boogey, I said it again. Don't know how to handle it, do you? That's okay. Neither do I. It's our culture and our upbringing. None of us has too much trouble getting the hang of being cute little kids or grubby teenagers or radiant newlyweds or bright young Turks or captains of industry or even reasonably well-adjusted grandmas and grandpas. But nothing in our role modeling or common experience adequately prepares us for the hard, cold inevitabilities of being old, lonely, and almost dead. Too bad. If there is any one experience for which we could use some heavy prepping, this is it. Recall how I said earlier that sex is our one great common denominator? Except for the great part, I missed it a mile. Fact is, there are a few hardy (or is it hard-up?) celibates, voluntary or otherwise, among us. They don't smile much, but they are out there just the same. Not so immortals. *De nada.* Zip. Zero. Nary a one of us gets out of this mess alive. Death is the single most predictable, most thoroughly intimidating fact of life we ever learn the hard way. The one absolute equalizer. We may come in as split as Herve Villechaize, Kareem Abdul-Jabbar, Jessica Lange, Arnold Schwarze-

whatever (big deal, he probably can't spell it correctly either), and this year's MS poster child, but we all go out stone cold.

This will not be a problem if you have used your freedom of choice wisely along the way. No mean trick. Sages, sayers of sooth, and everyday run-of-the-mill deep thinkers have been trying to help each other figure out how to do that ever since the original fun couple chomped into that first apple. Most of them have never gotten much farther along than Alfie. Not all the mysteries are locked away upstairs, you know. Some nag us from the word *go*. Why, for example, do ties so often seem to go to the wrong side in the never-ending battle of good versus evil? Why, as Joshua Liebman asked in his landmark *Peace of Mind*, is one picnicker's day in the park long and bright and sunny while another's gets hit by a cloudburst almost before it begins? Why are there starving babies? How could the same species have produced a Hitler and a Schweitzer; an Einstein and a Manson; Salk, Gandhi, and Mother Teresa along with Stalin, Jim Jones, and Gacy? What possible upper could come from having an all-pro halfback or an off-duty cop drown while trying to save someone else's kids? Where in the name of God or hell or both did the Holocaust fit? Is this prime mover of ours merely an unconcerned spectator at a chamber of horrors?

If you did not know better, you would think there was a sadistic streak buried somewhere beneath all that goodness and divinity. Some plan all right. Way beyond me. Yeah, I know. That's part of the plan. Guess all you can do is play out the hand that has been dealt as best you can and take what comes. As the wise beggar told the king who had promised untold fortune to anyone who could teach him perfect wisdom, "This too shall pass."

The strange thing about putting an end to the saga is that we assiduously avoid even thinking about it until we get close to doing it. Then we think about almost nothing else. And, of course, the more we think, the more we euphemize. *Kind Words: A Thesaurus of Euphemisms*, by Judith S. Neaman and Carole G. Silver, says we Americans are particularly adept at this essential skill.

At no other time in history has a culture created a more elaborate system of words and customs to disguise death so pleasantly that it seems a consummation devoutly to be wished. What used to be reserved for descriptions of eternal life and heaven is now used to describe embalmment, the funeral and the burial. It is here—and in Forest Lawn Memorial Park—that we are Loved Ones, cared for by a kind Bereavement Counselor, beautified forever by a Dermasurgeon and attired in a Slumber Robe, gently cradled in a Slumber Box and deposited in a Final Resting Place where we can forever hear the sound of recorded heavenly harps. Even our pets now go to Happy Hunting Grounds.

The entire proposition is what you might euphemistically call a porcelain receptacle full of biological effluvia, but if it helps, who am I to pop your happy balloon?

A—perhaps the—ranking authority on the subject, Dr. Elisabeth Kübler-Ross, has recorded the testimony of thousands who have revived after being declared legally dead. Their consensus paints the trip to the other side as a downright euphoric experience, one from which most regret having been recalled. Some of our all-time heaviest thinkers have agreed. Marcus Aurelius happytalked death as "a birthday in eternity." Noted campfire leader and stand-up philosopher Socrates couldn't understand what all the excitement was about. He expected death to trigger either "a re-union with all of your old friends or the best night's sleep you have ever had extended forever" and reasoned it would be hard to go wrong either way.

Understandably, not everyone has been as enthusiastic. As fellow patriots tried to ease his deathbed throes by whispering, "The angels are waiting," Ethan Allen replied, "Damn it, let them wait!" Some folks just never seem to get into the spirit of things. There are two explanations for that kind of spoilsport behavior. Three if you count not wanting to die. The big two are familiarity and kickthebucketophobia. Many reluctant passers are simply so comfortable with what is that they refuse to entertain the prospect of what will be. Others are flat-out scared $#!+£Σ $$. Some clinicians say the cause for alarm in both is more the unknown than the dying itself. Clinicians are full of it about some things, but they may have this one wired. The unknown frightens because it is, well, unknown. Ninety-nine times out of a hundred, dark rooms and eerie noises and strangers with gnarled hair turn out to be nothing more than dark rooms, eerie noises, and strangers with gnarled hair. It is conditioned response to the 1 percent exceptions that gets us where we live. This, too, may be part of the plan. Without fear we might also be without the good sense to allow our allotted string to play itself out, and both methods of passive resistance are preferable to rushing things for the wrong reasons.

Everyone needs some kind of ultimate answer to run by. For good old Alfie and me, it is the only four-letter word that doesn't seem to get used anymore. LOVE. Love cuts through the hassles, harangues, and doubts of gloom as nothing else can. Best of all, it is forever.

One out of three isn't bad.

Dr. Brenda Clorfene Solomon, whom you met earlier in the doctor's office, says the keys to living happy are having something to do, someone to love, something to hope for. Of course they are. And their reverse applies to dying before you have to. Those who lose purpose, love, and hope lose the will (or the force or whatever pop shrinks are calling it these days) to live. They give up. They die emotionally long before they die physically. They make one hell of an argument for a heaven where hope really can spring eternal.

Epilogue

The danger in a lower-case "This Is Your Life" run like this is the impression it can leave that the writer takes himself pretty seriously and expects the reader to do the same. No way. What I do take seriously is what I have been able to learn from you. And that is that most of us spend so much time buried in the guilt and regrets of our long-gone, irretrievable past or worrying about and fearing the unknown and unknowable future that we cannot enjoy the now that is becoming then. Live now. To live is to love. Vice versa.

Be seeing you . . . out there . . . up there . . . somewhere . . . maybe.

Conscious Resources

Blastfield, Jean F. *Hellraisers, Heroines, and Holy Women.* New York: St. Martin's Press, 1981.

Carruth, Gorton, and Associates. *The Encyclopedia of American Facts and Dates.* New York: Crowell, 1972.

Dickson, Paul. *Words: A Connoisseur's Collection of Old and New, Weird and Wonderful, Useful and Outlandish Words.* New York: Delacorte Press, 1982.

Dunkling, Leslie Alan. *First Names First.* New York: Universe, 1977.

Morris, Scot. *The Book of Strange Facts and Useless Information.* Garden City, N. Y.: Doubleday, 1979.

Perlongo. *The Everyday Almanac.* New York: Ace.

Tarshis, Barry. *The Average American Book.* New York: Signet, 1981.

Wallechinsky, David, Wallace, Amy, and Wallace, Irving. *The Book of Lists* (vol. 1, 2, and 3). New York: William Morrow, 1977–1983.

Chicago Tribune.